THE
IMMIGRANT
GARDEN

~ Letters ~

CAROLINE WOOD

SECOND EDITION

Original cover and book design by
Kathryn E. Campbell, 2005.
Author photograph: Dean Wood.
Book design 2017 by Grace Peirce and
Stephanie Voss Nugent.

Printed in the United States of America
Published in 2017 by:
Great Life Press
Rye, New Hampshire 03870
www.greatlifepress.com

ISBN: 978-1-938394-29-4
Library of Congress Control Number: 2017953312

*F*or my parents
John & Patricia Sprinzl
who taught me
what it means to love
and be brave.

"Of all the wonderful things
in the wonderful universe of God,
nothing seems to me more surprising
than the planting of a seed
in the blank earth and
the result thereof."

~ Celia Thaxter

from *An Island Garden*

ACKNOWLEDGMENTS
- First Edition -

Many thanks to Sarah Cadigan, who read all the drafts of this novel (and there were many) and who along with my mother, Pat Sprinzl, kept telling me I could do it. Also to Marvin Kaye, many thanks for his help in editing and his invaluable suggestions. You would not know of Mr. John Burrows if not for Marvin Kaye. For Leslie Roth and Leslie Slape, thank you both for your contribution to the garden. Many thanks to Lola Vestal for her important support and thanks to Steven Barnes, Tananarive Due, Brenda Cooper, Connie Dawley, and Audrey Hoffman for your encouragement.

For my husband's understanding I am very grateful. Dean stood by me for the three years it took to write this story and encouraged me to hold on when I thought I was going to be thrown from the roller coaster ride of rewrites. I do think though he could have laughed more over the funny parts of the manuscript – but then I must remember it was usually well past midnight when I'd emerge from my studio and thrust new pages into his hands. He was a good sport to read them at that time of night. And come to think of it, he often did laugh and shed a tear.

Always, I am grateful to the many audiences

who have loved the play version of this story. Your joy has been mine, and your enjoyment my encouragement. Thank you all.

A special thank you to Virginia Urrutia who inspired me no end.

PREFACE
- First Edition -

Dear Reader,

I have been thinking for a long time what I would write to you – what I would say about why I wrote this story. I can do best, I think, by using the metaphor of the garden. It seems I so often best understand life through the metaphor.

I believe the discovery of self is often a journey taken alone in the dark, not unlike the seed. It is in this darkness and in this stillness where growth begins, where strong stems and fragrant blossoms are envisioned and born – where the possibilities *that are us* are known though not yet seen.

Like the flower garden in this story, I am an immigrant from England. I left the small town of Beverley in Yorkshire, England with my family when I was ten years old and adjusted to the southern California suburbs, which in 1963 were slower-paced than they are these days.

When we were children in England, we went on nature walks during school. The smell of fresh English soil after a good rain is a fond memory, and even now I cannot help putting out my tongue and enjoying some of the gritty dirt that is on my hands while gardening.

I believe when we want growth, opportunities jump at the chance to be chosen. I would think an opportunity would be lost without someone to take advantage of it. I would think it would be downright miserable.

Opportunities though are not always found lying on the surface of things. We must dig in the dirt and go into the dark to find them. (You'll recognize something like those words later on). Let me tell you about the beginning of *The Immigrant Garden*. It started out as something small, not unlike a seed – a thirty-minute play consisting of eight letters.

In 1989 I was the owner of a large used bookshop. Inside was a little English style teashop where we served lunch. A friend who belonged to The Jane Austin Society in Portland, Oregon, asked if the Society members could come to the café and have a high tea (which means all those tiny sandwiches and tarts and pastries and, of course, scones). They would need me to present some kind of a half-hour program. I said, "Maybe I'll write something." At this time I had played around with writing. I had written some poems and two children stories.

This is where Sarah Cadigan comes in. In the beginning she was a stranger who walked into my bookshop asking if I needed some help at the shop. She had extensive experience in bookselling. Yes, I could use the help, but at that time my husband and I were the only employees,

I explained to her. She smiled and thanked me. She was walking toward the door, when I felt something distinctly like a tap on my shoulder. It got my attention. I watched as she opened the door, and then I heard myself telling her to come back on Monday and we would talk.

Well, talk we did, and we are friends to this day. Unknown to me at the time, Sarah had worked as an actor in London (oh, I forgot to tell you she's English). I worked on *The Immigrant Garden* at home in the evening and would bring in that night's work to the bookshop the next morning. Sarah would take a cup of tea, a scone, and my writing down into the basement (more books) and read. She would come upstairs with a big smile on her face. "Oh, it's lovely, Caroline!"

Sarah read Mrs. Beauchamp's letters to me, and I was shocked – I was standing in front of Mrs. Louise Beauchamp of White Cottage, Yorkshire. I never imagined such magic could happen. I knew I did not make this magic. I had made a space for it, and the magic had come.

Deana Martinson worked in my café. She was forty at the time and a good sport, and she played an amazing French horn. Wearing a 1910 era costume and smiling her endearing smile, Deana transformed herself into a seventeen-year-old Miss Cecily Barnes. My mom made the English pastries and I the sandwiches, and the tea and play were a huge success!

In 1990 a friend told me about a readers

theatre in New York City that was holding a playwriting competition. Why don't you enter a play, she said. I had by then written three more scripts and produced them in the dinner theatre setting in our little café. I packed up my three new plays, and it was only on second thought that I added *The Immigrant Garden.*

Three months later, I came home from the bookshop to find a message on my phone from a Mr. Marvin Kaye of The Open Book Readers Theatre. *The Immigrant Garden* was a finalist and would be produced as a showcase production. It was a bright sunny day; I remember because I was so excited that I went running through the waist-high grass of our pasture. I could have flown!

Then I started thinking . . . hmm if this man is so impressed with my play maybe it's because he doesn't get out very much. You know, maybe he just doesn't know what good writing really is. When later we spoke on the phone, we were both in for a surprise. I learned that Mr. Kaye was the artistic director of The Open Book and a well-published author who taught creative writing at NYU. Mr. Kaye's surprise was that I sounded very different on the phone than he had imagined I would. What did you expect, I asked? He said he thought I would be more the age of Mrs. Beauchamp. Louise is in her seventies; I was thirty-nine. He explained it was because of the wisdom in the play. I accepted this compliment, sharing it with that mysterious magical something that had met me in the sacred place of creativity and discovery and knowing.

I went to New York to see the play, and it was there I met another Louise Beauchamp, Beverly Fite Hanson. Sarah is from London, so naturally she had performed with a London accent. But Beverly used a Yorkshire accent. I was stunned, for it was like listening to the much-loved grandmother I had left behind in England.

Then the year 2001 rolls around, and I enroll in a video-making class at a community college a half-hour's drive from my home. Honestly, I would not have signed up for the class if I hadn't been told that the instructor was C. Tad Devlin, a film producer who had worked on some big Hollywood movies.

Most of the people in the class were technical people, wanting to know how to use their cameras and get good sound and such things. I was the only writer. So when Mr. Devlin asked each of us to bring in a short script, I was the only one with an original script. The class voted to produce mine – *The Immigrant Garden*.

Turns out, Mr. Devlin doesn't do many things small, so as I was adapting the stage play into a screenplay, he told me to keep writing until we had a full-length script. I wasn't sure how I felt about this. *The Immigrant Garden* was my first-born. It was fragile, so little, and so MINE!

We made the film on beautiful locations here

in southwest Washington. We used local talent, except for Mrs. Beauchamp. Beverly Hanson came from New York to be our Louise Beauchamp.

After the film, I was exhausted – for a year. Really. But there was something in me that wouldn't rest. The screenplay I wrote for the film had concentrated on Cecily's life. Now I wanted to know more about Mrs. Beauchamp. How did Louise know that *flowers are medicine for a longing soul?* The only way I was going to find out was to write it out. You must know this about me – I write because I want to know, not because I know.

My wish for you is that you come to hear the voices of these two women and know and trust them as I do and that you will call them friends. The story is fiction, but I tell you, it is an authentic tale in which there is not a single lie.

Sincerely,
Caroline Wood
Longview, Washington
2005

PREFACE
- Second Edition -

Dear Reader,

Twelve years have passed since I wrote the Preface to the First Edition, and *The Immigrant Garden*, as gardens are known to do, has spread its seed and roots beyond the garden wall. This new growth has come about because Stephanie Nugent is determined in her searches for what she desires. Stephanie is the artistic director of the Artists' Collaborative Theatre Of New England (ACT ONE), and we have become quite good friends, she and I.

In October 2016 she was searching for a play about a garden that could be performed in readers theatre style to open her 2017 season. This search led her to the First Edition of *The Immigrant Garden ~ Letters*. But there were too many letters for the stage. Might we collaborate on a stage adaptation, she asked, choosing letters that could play well in the two-hour allotted time for a theatre presentation?

I felt a familiar tap on my shoulder. I listened. By the time Stephanie found me, through contacting a theatre in my hometown that had just produced one of my plays, she had read the book many times over, and her affection for both Louise and Cecily was equal to mine – and that is saying quite a lot.

It was no easy task to track me down. In our first phone conversation, I remember Stephanie asked me, "Are you hiding?" And in a way I suppose I was. I had no website, nothing at all that would lead someone to me. I wasn't intentionally hiding; I just wasn't leaving many tracks.

Stephanie said, "I have to ask you something. Are you willing to go back to this story and work with me? Is it still alive for you?" I needed no hesitation to consider the question. These women and this story are etched in my heart and soul and will be forever.

Just before we ended that first phone conversation, I happened to mention to Stephanie that I had written a full-length novel of the story of *The Immigrant Garden* – still in manuscript form, unpublished. You see, even after writing the *Letters*, I wanted to know more. "Send it to me!" she said. I did and she was smitten by the much more detailed world of Cecily and Louise captured in the novel.

Over this past winter we have woven together the letters and passages from the novel, tracing the essential arc of this story. The two-act stage adaptation was completed this spring, and ACT ONE presented the play's premiere performances in June 2017 at the West End Studio Theatre in Portsmouth, New Hampshire. *The*

Immigrant Garden ~ Letters played to full houses, receiving standing ovations, heartfelt praise from audiences, and glowing reviews.

But then something unexpected happened. The phone calls began: "How can I get a copy of the book?" "I've been on the phone with Amazon, and they can't find any copies of Ms. Wood's book." "I went to Barnes & Noble, but they say there are no copies of the book available." "I want a copy of *The Immigrant Garden* for my bedside table . . . for my grandmother . . . for my grandson . . . for my friends who are gardeners . . ."

I shouldn't have been surprised. This story has had a special magic – its own Life Force – from the very beginning. A mysterious magical something that meets one in the sacred place of creativity and discovery and knowing.

So, of course, we immediately went to work on the Second Edition of *The Immigrant Garden ~ Letters*. Please know, Dear Reader, this book you hold in your hands has been touched by magic and good fortune and a great deal of love. Enjoy! And there will be more to come. The novel will be the next adventure Stephanie and I will take together!

I have a strong notion that our hearts know more than we are aware of. Yes, I was still and quiet these past few years. Like a seed. Was I hiding? Or was I waiting for Stephanie?

Since the First Edition of *Letters*, we sold our old farmhouse beside the Columbia River. I now live in a 600 square foot cabin along the Willappa Hills in southwest Washington with my husband, Dean, and our dog, Pippi, and our cats, Cooper and Little One. And our two chickens. The air is scented with fir and cedar trees and all those magical, mystical plants that grow from ancient fallen trees and rich loamy soil. A perfect place to work on a novel!

I hope you enjoy this new Second Edition. I'm very pleased with it. I shall imagine we are reading it together and that we are enjoying the company of those I never tire of.

Fondly,
Caroline
July 2017

Cecily Barnes

*"Be relentless in your search, for what it is you desire
seeks you with the same passion with which you seek it!"*

~ Louise Beauchamp to Cecily Barnes

February 1910

Coreopsis, Plains
Dwarf Bicolor
Coreopsis tinctoria (Calla...

Poppy Iceland
Nudicaule...

Lavender
Hidcote Dwarf
Lavandula angustifolia

Perennial
(Zones 5-9)
Blooms late
spring to
summer
12" tall
Full sun

This improved,
dwarf variety of
Lavender stays
12" high and
is uniform and
compact. Very
deep purple, full
fragrant flowers.

Mrs Beauchamp's Mystical Flower Seed
and Herb Emporium

Delphinium
...tic Giant Blend

Perennial
Blooms spring
to early summer
3' - 6' tall
Full sun

Rural Route 3, Box 542
Oakville, Washington
U.S.A.
February 3, 1910

To: Mrs. Beauchamp's Mystical Flower Seed
    and Herb Emporium
    White Cottage
    York Lane, Bishop Burton
    Yorkshire, England

Dear Mrs. Beauchamp,

I am writing this letter in response to your catalogue, which I found in the basement of our dry goods store. Mr. Welks, our shopkeeper, tells me you are no longer in the business of selling seeds, but I wondered if you might consider selling some to me.

I am new to the world of mulch, bone meal, aphids, cutworm, and that shapeless drop of flesh, the slug, and could benefit from someone who is more familiar with these things than I.

I am particularly interested in wallflowers. The seeds I purchased through a Seattle company have failed me – a whole year of anxiously waiting and no blooms, not a single one. And then to make matters worse, my usual friends the sparrows scratched up my marigold seeds that took an entire afternoon to plant. I screamed at their feathered backs and threatened to take down their feeders.

And to make matters worse yet, the neighbor's ducks, which I normally adore, traipse through my garden when-ever it pleases them! I shoo them away and threaten them with the most horrid things! Do I sound too impatient to be a gardener?

Do you have any hollyhock and perhaps some foxglove, larkspur, and dahlias? I would be interested in purchasing some. Mr. Welks told me that his grandmother had delphinium that grew twelve feet! I cannot imagine looking so high up at a flower. It sounds wonderful though, and if you have some that can grow that high, can you send me them please?

Yours Very Sincerely
Miss Cecily Barnes

Post Script. In your catalogue you have written,
"Flowers are Medicine For a Longing Soul."
Is this really true?

White Cottage
York Lane, Bishop Burton
Yorkshire, England
19th February 1910

Dear Miss Cecily Barnes,

You remind me of my little brook in late
November when it is full and nearly overflowing.
You are young and either very beautiful or
painfully plain, for passion does not come from
that place in between.

Your letter has broken my solitude, and for
the slight ripple in my clear pool of stillness I
am grateful, for you ask nothing from me but my
seeds, which I give to you freely. In my old age
I have turned quite eccentric and refuse to do
anything that I do not want to.

You asked if you lacked the patience to
be a gardener. It is not what you lack that is of
concern; it is what you possess. And you possess
a passion to grow flowers, and passion is the
purest form of ambition or love.

My child, I hope you have not dug up your
wall-flower seeds. Wallflowers are biennial and
therefore bloom the second year, not the first. As
for your feathered friends, the sparrows, I suggest
laying some newspaper over your freshly planted

seeds until they germinate and you see their pale green shoots. Then take the paper off, and after a couple of days in the sun, the tender shoots will turn a rich green and shall no longer tempt the sparrows' appetite.

As for your neighbor's ducks, you might remind your neighbor, in a neighborly way, that you have planted some fresh seeds and can't have them trampled. If this does not produce results, do what good neighbors sometimes must: put up a fence. Along with keeping ducks out, you will see that the fence will serve another purpose – your enclosed flower garden will take on the atmosphere of a sanctuary.

I am no longer in the business of selling seeds, but I have put together a parcel for you. Find the following and their instructions: hollyhock, Althea rosea (one can never have too many); Iceland poppy, Papaver nudicaule; golden columbine, Aquilegia chrysantha; asters, Aster Amellus; sweet William, Dianthus barbatus; cosmos, Cosmos bipinnatus; hop, H. lupulus; picotee pinks (of the carnation family), Dianthus caryophyllus; sweet pea, Lathyrus odoratus; sweet rocket, Hesperis matronalis; golden banner coreopsis (of the daisy family); my prized sunflowers, Helianthus; and a cutting from my much loved lavender, Lavendula.

I am also sending you a rather pathetic looking, twisted thing – have no fear, it holds within its mangled form the beautiful dahlia! Plant it in a sunny, well-drained spot and dispense plenty barnyard manure.

Work the soil until it crumbles easily between your fingers. Good soil needs to be light and airy so the roots of your flowers can easily spread and acquire the water they need. Mix some lime with your soil and, if it is at all possible, purchase the finest ground lime you can so the active oxide will work at a faster rate. Lime alone will not make a rich soil for flowers. Good rotted barn manure is best. Spread it an inch to an inch and a half thickness over your soil.

Enclosed as well are some of my best delphinium seed. Your Mr. Welks is quite correct. The stonewall surrounding my garden is well over twelve feet, and the villagers walking down York Lane often see the blue and purple tips of my delphinium swaying happily above the wall. You say a flower that tall sounds wonderful but you cannot imagine looking so high up at a flower? Imagine it, Miss Cecily Barnes, for it exists!

Best of luck!

Most Sincerely,
Mrs. Louise Beauchamp

Post Script. Yes, it is most definitely true: flowers are medicine for a longing soul. I often hold lengthy conversations with my flowers. Mind you though, I would not have engaged in conversation if they had not started it first.

5

Rural Route 3, Box 542
Oakville, Washington
U.S.A.

Dear Mrs. Beauchamp,

When I received by post your letter and parcel of seeds, I was thoroughly delighted! The instructions you have written on each package leave no room for question. You have thought of everything. I never expected so much and am taken aback with delight!

While holding between my fingers the delicate vessels of root, stem, and blossom, I am reminded by some whispering thought that my garden shall be the daughter of yours!

Mr. Welks has given me my very own gardening tools. He said they were last year's stock and he needed to be rid of them. I do not see any difference between last year's stock and this, but I am now the owner of a spade, a spading fork, a square-top hoe, a rake, a hand trowel, and a stainless steel watering can (with a pretty red handle), all compliments of "Rufus T. Welks Dry Goods Store Extraordinaire!"

I have spent the last three days broadening the width and length of my garden. So instead of being twenty by twenty, it is now twenty-five by fifty feet. It is three and a half cartwheels across and seven down! Perfect! I worked in the lime and barnyard manure and have raked the hard soil soft – well, softer than it was.

I've come across the cutworm, Mrs. Beauchamp. I counted ten! Is that a lot? Do you have a remedy that perhaps persuades them permanently never to return?

This evening I cleared the shelving below the window in the storage shed of cans of paint and by lantern light filled low flat trays with sifted soil and, per your instructions, planted the new arrivals.

At this late hour my body is tired, and yet I cannot sleep. In my imagination I see you reading these very words at the very moment I am writing them!

But Mrs. Beauchamp, you have forgotten to include an invoice. Please tell me how much I owe you. Your lifestyle sounds very bohemian, living alone and talking with flowers. I, myself, well you said I was young, and I suppose seventeen is young. But my father insists that I ought to like boys by now, especially the boys he brings home to dine with us.

My father is a teacher at a boys' academy. But why should I like boys when I find them total and complete bores. I find "intellectuals" extremely boring. They lift their noses high and quote Sir Francis Bacon or Lucretius, but always the same passages over and over again, until I imagine my mouth is moving to form the words before their voices wallow up from their throats.

And when I ask them for an original thought, they look at me as though I have just inquired whether their undergarments were adjusted properly. "Why," they say, "all thought is original, Miss Barnes. Whatever could you possibly mean?"

It is then I develop a dreadful headache and insist the only remedy is a cup of chamomile tea and my own bed, where I shall agonize for hours before finally finding escape in a fitful sleep.

I confess I cause my father a fair amount of displeasure, but if he would quit bringing students home for reward dinners, I would be kinder, and I am certain he would be the happier for it.

But you, Mrs. Beauchamp, I imagine full of grace and glowing countenance with eyes that see into the souls of men. And your garden moves across my mind as though it were a dream dreamt long ago and only remembered in fragments. And you have heard the voice of flowers! Tell me, what sort of things do flowers say?

Please write soon,

Your Friend,
Miss Cecily Barnes

White Cottage
York Lane, Bishop Burton,
Yorkshire, England

Dear Miss Cecily Barnes,

I took your letter and a glass of sherry out to my garden and announced the exciting news to the flowers. They are happy to know that their seeds sailed safely across the Atlantic Ocean and landed in your caring hands.

About this inquiry of the invoice, I have no need of money and would feel uncomfortable accepting payment for something I do not, in its truest sense, own.

Find enclosed the following seeds and their instructions – Canterbury Bell, Narcissus 'Butter and Eggs', Codlins-and-Cream, Jonquils, Crown Imperials, and Scarlet Lychnis. The Canterbury Bells have a preference for semi-shade; expect blooming in June and July. I have sent you white, blue, and pink bells. An English flower garden is never without them.

Also you will find enclosed the sketch and dimensions of a propagating frame that you will find useful if you do not already have one.

By the way, do you have toads in your garden, Cecily? I suggest acquiring some if you do not. I purchase mine from Covent Garden Market in London for a shilling apiece. Toads are lovers of noxious insects and are really quite pleasant fellows to have about.

You mentioned the cutworm. Lime turned into the soil is recommended, as is diatomaceous earth. But truly the only certain way is to dig them up and be done with them. Remember they do their nasty work at night. Be ready by dusk!

"What do my flowers say?" you ask. I would do best to quote your Mr. Ralph Waldo Emerson:

> *Nature is a language, and every new fact one learns is a new word; but it is not a language taken to pieces and dead in the dictionary, but the language put together into a most significant and universal sense. I wish to learn the language – not that I may know a new grammar but that I may read the great book which is written in that tongue.*

Mr. Emerson wrote that in his journal in 1833 and I am just now discovering its truth. I suppose when I say I "talk" with flowers, what I really mean is to touch, to communicate, to let something be known.

One morning, while weeding a bed of Shirley poppies, a thought, quite clearly, came to me, like a sailing vessel appearing on the horizon. It said, *"Do you understand that I cannot acknowledge your greatness until I confess my own?"* Well, I must say I looked over my shoulder to see who was there speaking. So vivid was the thought that I fancied I had heard it in voice.

I do believe this is what your Mr. Emerson must have meant, for indeed I heard no nouns or verbs on that morning. What I heard was beyond spoken language. Instead, it was the very breath of thought, and I believe thought is at the root of all things.

I went inside and wrote down the announcement, for that is what I felt it was. I often repeat it to myself, and it seems I never tire of its wisdom and solace.

> Best wishes,
> Mrs. Louise Beauchamp

Post Script. Tomorrow the sun crosses the celestial equator. It is the Vernal Equinox, Miss Barnes. The first day of Spring!

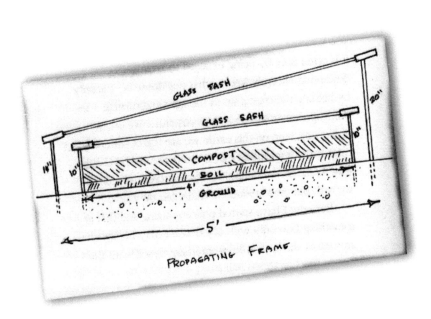

GLASS SASH

GLASS SASH

20"

COMPOST

10"

SOIL

18"

10"

4'

GROUND

5'

PROPAGATING FRAME

Spring

If you did not spade up your garden in the fall, let no more time elapse – put in a thick layer of compost or well aged manure. Spade it deeply into the soil, spreading it evenly. The common spade and spading fork are your best tools for this job. Your objective will be to prepare a deep, loose friable seedbed, to bring plant food up to the surface, and to bury the manure deep into the soil. Finish this off with a good raking over, making certain all stones and twigs are removed. Keep your eye open for the arrival of creeping phlox, dog-tooth violets, hardy candytuft, and the sweet scented lilac!

The Garden Club's Spring Tea will be held at Mrs. Helen Curtis' cottage instead of the vicarage. The date and time are the same. Helen promises currant scones!

My flower garden often becomes my world – my world beneath a magnifying glass. For all creatures of the garden are all the creatures of the world. I see in the velvety face of the pansy all children ever born and in the heart of a gillyflower all the souls that ever soared.

Mrs. Louise Beauchamp
Newsletter ~ 3 April 1899

My Flowers – and Herbs
— Cecily Barnes 1910

Common Name	Botanical	Height	Growth Cycles
Aster	Callistephus chinensis	12 to 18 inches	annual (wild aster are perennial) (likes poor soil)
Cosmos	C. bipinnatus	8 to 10 ft high	mostly annual - some per
Canterbury Bells	(= Chimney BellFlower) - blue. C. pyramidalis	4 ft	Blooms June + July biennial (some annual varieties)
" "	C. medium	4 ft	biennial
Hollyhock	Althea rosea	flowers in early July 12 ft	biennial or semi-perennial Blooms late summer
Phlox	P. PANICULATA (most familiar)	6 ft	PERENNIAL
LAVENDER	Lavandula	Blooms mid to late summer	(herb) - Shrubby
SnapDragon	Antirrhinum	8 to 12 in high Flowers from early	PERENNIAL - can be treated as an annual
Sweet Pea	Lathyrus odoratus	6 ft needs support	annual
DAHLIA	History - Discovered in Mexico in the 16th Century by Spanish.	18 to 24 inches	store tubes over winter PERENNIAL
Shirley Shire Poppy	RHOEAS COMMON field Poppy	3 ft	herb - ANNUAL (some PERENNIAL
DelPhinium	Commonly known as Larkspur D. cheilanthum	8 ft Blooms summer!	herb - ANNUAL or Perennial
Sweet William	Dianthus barbatus	June - July 18 inches	herbaceous Perennial
"	(Tickseed) (Daisy Family) Compositae	4 (or 1½ ft) ft	PERENNIAL (herb)
Golden-banner Coreopsis	C. drummondi	12 ft !!	PERENNIAL
Foxglove	(Part of the Figwort family) D. purpurea	3 to 5 ft Spring	(herb) biennial or perennial
Columbine	Aquilegia	Blooms April or May	PERENNIAL (HERB)
Rosemary	Rosmarinus officinalis	6 ft ?	PERENNIAL
	MY IMMIGRANT GARDEN		

Rural Route 3, Box 542
Oakville, Washington
U.S.A.

Dear Mrs. Louise Beauchamp,

I rose before the sun and in my nightdress
and bare feet knelt before the first sight of green
shoots. I dare not tell anyone but you of the
purest joy I feel at this moment!

And thank you ever so much for the new
seeds you sent. I gave them a warm American
welcome. Per your instructions, I have planted
these newest arrivals in trays until they germinate.
I wonder if they will recognize their relatives from
your garden?

What began with me as an inquiry has now
turned into a gift beyond my imagination. Your
generosity waves in the air like a bright yellow
kite on the bluest of blue-sky days. Thank you!

I have pleaded to be excused from
dinner tonight and have my evening meal in my
bedroom, as I know my father is expecting a
dinner guest – one of those lofty intellectuals with
sweaty palms and crooked necktie, I'm certain.
But my father wouldn't relent, and I am not happy
about it. I dislike obeying my father's wishes

when they are not my own. But unfortunately, equally so, I do so like to please him.

Why must I be capable of so many opposing feelings? I find myself in the middle of what, I'm not certain. I am not entirely knowing, but I can imagine that life would be far less tiresome if I were capable of only one way of seeing, one way of thinking, and one way of feeling.

Oh dear, it's time to set the table. Please feel sorry for me, Mrs. Beauchamp. Your sympathy shall be my salvation.

Affectionately,
Cecily Barnes

White Cottage
York Lane, Bishop Burton
Yorkshire, England

Dear Cecily Barnes,

You indeed have my sympathy. But you
are young and therefore have no need of it, for
though unaware, you are brave and shall survive
quite well.

Though you do seem outnumbered, my dear.
And for that I am sorry, for the conversations of
men are often just that. I am certain that men
and women can *share* a conversation, it is only
that one wonders if one is having the *same*
conversation. But as with all other things in this
wonderful world, men and boys are necessary – I
mean that in the broadest terms.

I, too, am feeling somewhat outnumbered
– by caterpillars! They are such dear creatures,
but their appetite has already doomed one of
my pear trees and is threatening an apple. I am
presently gathering information as to the best
way to persuade them to take up other lodgings.
Preferably in Wales!

Did I tell you while gardening it makes good
sense to put a sprig of lavender beneath your
bonnet? It is said to keep headaches away. I have

practiced the habit for years and found its purpose quite useful. And if you are interested in making lavender water, here is my recipe:

> 23 ounces of distilled water
> 2 ounces of vodka
> 1 ounce of dried lavender

Last August, when the sun seemed determined to scorch us to cinders over here, I poured an entire bottle of it over my head. We are not used to such extreme heat in this part of England, and I found it most uncomfortable.

Lavender is a great favorite of mine, and I'm not content with it growing only in my garden. I pot it up and bring it into the cottage and put it on my windowsill. It is quite pleasing. Last evening past, the air was so still I could hear the water running in my little brook. I opened the windows and in minutes was surrounded by the heady sweetness of my lavender.

It is strange in a way, for the fragrance suggests to me another time, a world beyond time perhaps. And for a moment I am there in a place that seems so familiar, so known to me. But no sooner than the experience begins, it quickly fades, and I am left with an armful of nothingness and a sense of longing.

Have you ever studied mysticism, my dear? In my younger years I traveled extensively. It was the Far East that captured me! Oh, I was an eager prisoner, meditating with mystics and sleeping beneath the stars at the feet of ancient shrines! I suppose this is where I might have picked up some of my queer ways, or as you say – bohemian.

I am sending you a lovely edition of Emerson's *Essays*. It is a signed copy that once belonged to my mother. I hope you will like it and can find a place in your heart for it.

I will now offer you some advice you might not be so willing to accept. You say you wish there were but one way of seeing, one way of thinking, and one way of feeling. But if this were so, how then could you know what you feel and think were truly your own? It is often only by being exposed to what we do not desire that we truly know what our desire is. It is only by holding the crystal up to the light and turning it in our fingers that we see all its facets, its true structure. We are not unlike anything on this earth; we are full of different parts and complexities. That is our structure. This is our way. As the crystal catches the light and reflects it, so do we, with our own uniqueness, create our own light.

But now I have started philosophising, and that is something I do only with my flowers. May I fancy you are one of them, or at least, entertain myself with the thought?

Affectionately,
Louise Beauchamp

19

Rural Route 3, Box 542
Oakville, Washington
U.S.A.

Dearest Louise,

How would you doubt anything less? Indeed I am one of your flowers! Bring me to your face and let me kiss your cheek. I cannot express in words what you have given me. I asked for seeds and you gave me a new way to see the world.

I received your parcel and squealed with delight. Your mother's book signed by Ralph Waldo Emerson himself! Your mother's book and then yours and now mine! I have read Emerson's essays in school but to hold in my hand a volume in which he himself signed his name is beyond words. Thank you from my heart, where this volume shall always be kept.

I decided to copy out my favorite essays. I started with my very favorite, "Self-Reliance." I had been writing for no more than twenty minutes when it struck me! My pen dropped from my hand! I made no effort to retrieve it but instead read aloud the next sentence – which only amplified its significance! I quote:

A man is relieved and gay when he has put his heart into his work and done his best;

but what he has said or done otherwise shall
give him no peace. It is a deliverance which
does not deliver. In the attempt his genius
deserts him; no muse befriends; no invention,
no hope.

Do you see it, Louise? Not a "woman" or a
"she" or "her" to be found! Of course, I'm aware
that "man" is to mean all human beings, but not
all human beings are men. And I am certain that
Mr. Emerson meant to share his wisdom with
women as well as men.

So one might ask then, "why not be
satisfied?" I would reply – to address accurately
the person to whom one is speaking confirms the
authenticity of that person.

I cannot imagine a man thinking it acceptable
in the books he reads to be addressed as a
woman. He would find the joke tasteless and
accept only the severest of apologies – which he
would promptly reject!

I made all corrections in my own handwritten
copy of "Self-Reliance," replacing all the "he's"
with "she's." I am trusting my heart, vibrating to
that iron string!

Oh, Mrs. Beauchamp I must tell you, or
perhaps you can sense it? I am writing this
letter from my Sanctuary! My dear Mr. Burrows,
Handyman Extraordinaire of Oakville, was here
last week, replacing some shingles on the roof
of our house, while I was working on the fence
for my garden. He told me later that he had been

watching me as long as he would bear it before coming down.

I was wrestling with the west-facing section of fencing, when I saw Mr. Burrows climbing down his ladder. It was a warm day, and I thought he was going to the pump to get some water. But he didn't. Instead he came over to me and said:

"Miss Cecily, I know you wouldn't ask; that's why I'm offering to help you with your fence. I got the entire afternoon and tomorrow free. That means it wouldn't cost you a cent. You're doing a fine job, and most likely don't need my help . . . "

"Why, thank you," I said.

"Trouble is," he said, "are those posts."

"I don't have any posts," I said.

"Those'd be the ones," he said.

Well, I looked at him, and he looked back at me; then we both burst out laughing! By the end of the following afternoon, we had six posts dug in three feet deep. One for each corner and two in place for a gate. As I nailed up pickets, Mr. Burrows worked on the gate. We didn't talk about anything in particular; we just made passing comments on the general things of life. I rather liked that.

Now I spend deliciously long hours in my Sanctuary, studying the botanical names of my flowers. It is after a long while studying that I sometimes drift into a light sleep and hear myself whispering names such as – Erinus alpines,

Cosmos bipinnatus, Hunnemannia fumariaefolia, Mirabilis jalapa. I imagine nectar collecting on my lips, and I send out my tongue and taste the sweetness that has gathered there.

After a nap, when all the world seems smoothed out, I often sketch what I see when I first open my eyes. Sometimes it's a wren flying by or a humblebee or a blade of grass.

I am constructing the propagating frame. My father says he could do it easily, but I tell him I want to do it myself. He watches me from the house while I'm working on the frame. He can't stand it, you know – that I have a flower garden. He says I ought to be doing more constructive things with my time.

If you can believe it, he has asked Mr. Burrows to take down my garden fence. I fear, Louise, that my father has no idea who I am. I am invisible to him, and I only wish he were to me.

      Your Dearest Flower,
      Cecily

      Post Script. I have some uninvited guests in my garden. Do you have a potion for the removal of slugs?

White Cottage
York Lane, Bishop Burton
Yorkshire, England

Dearest Flower,

Oh my! Your intuition is serving you well,
for although I sent you Ralph Waldo Emerson's
Essays, you heard the voice of another, one whose
voice was not heard in her own day and shall not
perhaps be heard in my day or yours – Emerson's
aunt, Mary Moody Emerson. She was young
Emerson's tutor and philosophical benefactor.
      You will read Mary's words often guised as
Emerson's own. I believe you might have found
Mary Emerson interesting; everyone who met
her did. Mary both minded and did not mind
her words being quoted and not noted. She was
aware that a man's voice was able to find print
and readership, while a woman's voice was not
allowed to be whispered in a public debate.
      Mary Emerson wanted her life's work to
be shared and must have seen this as a way.
Emerson revered his aunt, but he did not know
where to put her, so that when he listed the ten
finest men he knew, she was among them! I
believe she will appreciate your straightening
out the gender of the essays.

You mentioned your frustration with your father, and it brought to mind my own father. We each stood a distance apart from one another, never certain who ought to make the first move. I am sad to say that neither one of us made any move. My father died without me knowing him and without him knowing me.

I consider this one of the greatest losses of my life. My father never showed any interest in my flower garden. He never entered the gate. I so much wanted him to, yet I never asked him. I often wonder what he would have said had I asked. But it does not matter any more what he would have said. It only matters that I did not ask.

I did not mean to go on about myself. Quite unexpected really. Not intentional. I've gotten myself into a bit of a melancholy mood now, or rather, a reflective mood. Let's leave it at that. Reflective. Without reflection we could know only the surface of life, and I believe the most interesting things in life lie just beneath the surface.

Do you have a pond in your garden? A pond will bring the damselfly, among other water nymphs. Expect a parcel of pond flower seeds in a few weeks – the scented pond lily, water hyacinth, water lobelia, swamp rose, and bog rosemary. If you would like shade around your pond (and I do recommend it), I suggest a green ash, a river birch, and perhaps a few shrubs such as sweet gale, leather leaf, and red osier dogwood.

A potion for the removal of slugs is one part sulfate of copper to four parts garden lime, dissolved in water. It is recommended that it be poured around the edge of your garden just after sunset. If that fails, a hunting expedition in the dark with a lantern is said to be the surest remedy.

As for my own potion, it consists of persuading the slugs onto my hand trowel and then sending them flying into the field beyond my garden. I always wish them a safe flight and a slow journey back. It is not difficult to love a butterfly, is it Cecily, for they give us no reason not to love them, while a slug gives us so many reasons. Which I suppose is why I cannot dislike them. When one thing is not compared to another, it is so much easier to see its beauty.

Affectionately,
Louise

Rural Route 3, Box 542
Oakville, Washington
U.S.A.

Dear Louise,

My fathers' pipe tobacco drifts from his open study window and crosses my garden. I hear the familiar whistle of the train as it crosses the trestle at the Chehalis River, and yet here in my garden I am away from all things familiar and together with all things new.

How is it possible to travel so far in mind while your body does not leave? But when I think of it in another way, it makes perfect sense! I have walked briskly up and down the paths of my garden, retrieving rake, hoe, or shovel (not to mention the watering can) more times than I am able to count – and that is not counting the morning and evening strolls! Certainly I have walked miles!

I am becoming fond of this mode of travel. It relies on no one, and there is no arriving or departing. I find myself sighing out of utter pleasure and ease. I suppose one could say a garden is hard work with all that weeding and mulching and turning over soil and all that bending over and getting down on your knees.

But would a lover who brings his beloved a cool glass of water on a warm day feel he is being burdened? No, it is an act of love, and the beloved feels the love with every act. Every footstep a prayer.

In your letter you told me about your father and then said, that you did not mean to go on about yourself. I go on about myself all the time. You do not. You must think me selfish sometimes. See, I'm already talking about myself when really my thoughts are full of you – you and your sadness. One of the greatest losses of your life you called it. And "it doesn't matter what he would have said it only matters that I did not ask." My dear Louise, I am hugging you. Feel my arms around you and my cheek against yours. I hope I do not add to your sadness by going on and on about my father. I try to leave him out of our conversation as much as possible. He says he finds it "interesting" that I'm carrying on a correspondence with you and that you are not charging me for your seeds. It's the way he says "interesting," Louise, as though this were an odd, obscure word hardly ever used in everyday speech.

Oh, Louise! The Iceland poppy! You should have warned me that I could be overcome by such beauty. I never imagined such a color as this existed. It is feeble to call it orange, but then all seems feeble when attempting to describe what is beyond reach of words. I hardly dare touch a petal, so delicate they are. But I do dare and am rewarded with a softness so pure my breath escapes me.

The blue asters have burst forth! This country I am in has such vivid colors – the color of dreams. The violet-blue petals of the aster sing, and oh, you cannot help but hum along!

The cosmos are arriving; their buds pop open, and the cosmos unfurl themselves into the world without a care! The sweet pea! How could I have lived this long and not breathed in this perfume? Like a rose it is but even more so.

I am certain when the flowers share their voices with me, they shall be speaking with English accents. I've come to think of my garden as an immigrant garden. The Dear Ones crossed an ocean and a continent to arrive at their new home. How more like a flower I would like to be. Must being brave be a conscious act? Cannot the act alone stand alone?

I've been working on a chart, "Enemies of the Garden." I made you a copy, not that you need advice from me. It's more me wanting you to see what I am doing, what I am up to. Oh, I'm such a naughty girl! Do you think in three weeks time, on the eve of Summer Solstice, I ought to light candles in a circle and dress like a druid and really roll my father's oats?! I wouldn't do that, but what delight there is in thinking of such peculiar acts in all their delicious details!

Louise, do you wear gloves when you garden? You haven't mentioned that you do, and I am supposing that iif you did wear gloves, that you would have advised me to do the same. I do not wear gloves. My father, (I am sorry to have to bring him up again), tells me I should wear gloves. As if he would know the ins and outs of being a gardener.

Oh, I have toads in my garden! I don't know how long they will stay, but the little neighbor boys, (Harry and George, eight and six respectively) took my offer of ten cents a toad quite seriously. I had eight at last count. I do enjoy them. As you say, "they are dear fellows to have about." I let Harry and George come into the garden to unload their "deliveries," and they were in the habit of lingering afterwards, so I told them they were welcome to join me in the garden – as long as they don't touch anything and don't talk. Oh, I'm a terrible person!

Oh, I was thinking of digging up another bed, but the soil is more clayey and doesn't break up easily. Any suggestions?

And if you have time, can you recommend some flowers well suited for window boxes?

I have finished the propagating frame and am using it to start the last seeds you sent me. Have you heard of "damping off?" I have no idea what it means, though it does sound like something I wouldn't like.

Your Dearest Flower,
Cecily

Post Script. I will dream of a pond in my garden
with damselflies and water nymphs. Nymphs,
those mythological spirits of nature said to be
beautiful maidens! Or perhaps they are
fascinating women such as Mary
Moody Emerson! I never
knew of her and now I
must know more!

Enemies of The Garden!

Aster	Black blister beetle, Thrips, Spotted cucumber beetle, grubs.
Barberry	Eight-spotted forester, Barberry webworm (Omphalocer dentosa)
Chrysanthemum...	Aphids, Mexican mealybug, Spittle bug
Columbine	Black stinkbug, Columbine skipper (Erynnis lucilius)
Cosmos	Six-spotted leafhopper, Red spider, Asiatic garden beetle
Geranium	Cabbage looper, Fuller's rose beetle, Cottony-cushion scale
Lilac	Lilac leaf miner (Gracilaria syringella) Scurfy Scale
Marigolds	Yellow wooly bear, cutworms, Garden flea hopper
Peony	Four-lined plant bug, Rose chafer (Macrodactylus subspinosus)
Phlox	White grubs Yellow woolly bear, Flower thrip
Hollyhock	Japanese beetle, Golden tortoise beetle, wire worms
Snapdragon...	Rose budworm (Pyrrhia umbra) Aphids, Verbena Moth
Honeysuckle	Long-tailed mealybug, Honeysuckle sawfly (Zaraea inflata)
Dahlia	Cocklebur billbug, European corn borer
Larkspur	Red aphids
Delphinium...	Cyclamen mite, Larkspur leaf miner (Phytomyza delphiniae)
Sweet Pea	Sowbug, spotted cucumber beetle, Four-lined plant bug

White Cottage
York Lane, Bishop Burton
Yorkshire, England

Dearest Cecily,

So, I should have warned you, should I? No,
the astonishment of beauty must come straight
at you without notice! We who love our flowers
never become immune to being overwhelmed by
beauty. Instead we make more room. Have no
fear; you will not pop but rather burst open and
show yourself!

You have been busy, Cecily. Your "Enemies
of the Garden" chart tells me you have been
doing your research. And I do want to know
what my Naughty Dearest Flower is up to. I think
you are having a grand time, and I'm certain
the flowers are enjoying you immensely! My
dear friend, Helen Curtis and I will celebrate the
summer solstice at a bonfire with a few of our
neighboring pagans and have a grand time as
well, I'm sure.

I have extensive books on garden pests and
have found a few species that you might want
to add to your list: enemies of the hollyhock are
spotted cucumber beetle, red banded leaf roller,

stalk borer and leafhoppers. Enemies of phlox
are Asiatic garden beetle and the golden tortoise
beetle (which is very beautiful). Watch out for the
verbena bud moth in your snapdragons. Moths,
our nighttime butterflies!

Prevention, of course, is the best strategy
against the enemies in the garden. Cut and burn
old stalks after the first frost. Rake away all debris.
If old stems are left on the plants that are infected,
nymphs will hatch and attack the new growth
in the spring. In the spring, watch for evidence
of the pests; if there is any indication of their
presence, or any question in your mind, dust the
plant with sulphur. I prefer a potion of one part
pyrethrum dust and three parts dusting sulphur.
Apply three times in the space of ten days.

I have found nicotine sulphate useful against
soft-bodied and sucking insects. This can be
prepared as both spray and powder. If you
prepare the spray, dissolve two tablespoons of
soap flakes into each gallon of water used. For
small quantities of nicotine sulphate, use one
to one and a fourth teaspoons to one gallon of
water. For larger quantities, use one fluid ounce to
eight gallons of water. Add the nicotine sulphate
immediately before spraying. If you are spraying
waxy or shiny leaves, add extra soap. And for
hardier insects, a little more nicotine sulphate
might be necessary.

I don't feel altogether good about being so
exact in my means of killing. But it brings out

the passion in me when I come across one of
my beloved flowers under siege of the enemy.
Flowers are helpless to defend themselves, and I
suppose I have taken it upon myself to be their
guardian. Guardian – gardener – there is little
difference in these words and none whatsoever in
their meanings.

I do, though, send a thought to "enemies" as
I pump away on my sprayer or smother the little
darlings with powder. I let them know that I am
sending them on to a better place, where at some
time in the future they might return as a flower
and understand my actions.

Our dear hollyhocks are often overtaken
with rust. Weekly applications of dusting sulphur
during rainy periods and every fortnight during
dry weather is a wonderful prevention . . . if
started early in the season. Mind, though that you
keep the sulphur off the flowers while in bloom.
If you do find rust, do not water with a sprinkler.
Surface irrigate only. This keeps the foliage dry
and prevents spores from being spread and
splashed about. Keep an eye out for cyclamen
mite and red spider. And snout beetles are
nothing to shake a stick at either.

The term "damping off" is the condition (in
this regard perhaps I should have warned you)
of the rapid rotting at the base of seedlings.
Seedlings may be "damped off" in such a young
stage that they never emerge from the soil. Always
make certain your seedlings have good drainage.

I have been meaning to tell you more about how to bring help to poor soil. Although lime begins to work in the garden the first year, expect better results in the second, third, and even fourth year.

Lime is best applied in the fall, or if not, then in early spring. Keep away from poultry and sheep manure if you can; they expel rapid amounts of nitrogen, which grows the plant abundantly at the expense of the blossom. If all you have is poultry manure, mix it together with one-third pail-full of super phosphate and a little quart of muriate of potash. Wood ashes contain from 2-4% potash and 28-30% equivalent of lime. Do not mix together poultry manure and ashes because the nitrogen from the poultry will be wasted through chemical reaction.

Your sketch of the sow bug is quite impressive. I recognized it straight away. You needn't have sent the specimen, which although wrapped in tissue did not remain so. There is something you ought to know about this curious little creature. It is not an insect at all but a crustacean and is related to the lobster and crayfish. The garden is full of mystery.

And you have your toads now as well! Your young Masters Harry and George also sound like pleasant fellows to have about . . . as long as they don't talk or touch anything. Oh, you are a wicked one, you are.

Moving on. So, you're interested in flower boxes! My favorite flowers for a sun-facing box is the red geranium, which is sometimes called cranesbill and belongs to the genus pelargonium. Geraniums are very easy to propagate by cuttings. Petunias also love the sun but not hot afternoon sun. If you are very lucky, you might spy a hummingbird moth making regular visits to your petunias. Fuchsia, begonias mixed together with myrtle, and English ivy are always in my shade window boxes.

I'm sending on to you a box of old newsletters that I was in the habit of writing and mailing out to my customers. You might find some useful information in them.

You would like to know more about Mary Emerson, would you? She was a self-possessed woman who was fiercely passionate about gaining knowledge and did not let anything stand in the way of what she desired – with striking singularity. Her passion gave her immense energy, so that when she was eighty years of age she was carrying on vigorous discussions with young people. She wanted to know what they were thinking, what they were reading. She saw herself as a bee buzzing from flower to flower, collecting knowledge.

Thoreau believed her to be a genius and sought out her company whenever she visited her nephew, Waldo. She trusted that knowledge could be grasped through one's imagination.

She read widely and voraciously. In her famous *Almanacks*, she let her mind loose and allowed her imagination to run amok, and in this way she reached her genius.

Her life was most unconventional. She chose not to marry, and because she cared for an elderly relative in her youth, she inherited a house with acreage when she was a young woman. She rented out the property, which provided her with an income and freedom. She traveled alone from town to town in search of bigger libraries. She sought acclaimed orators who left her in blissful raptures.

I am certain Mary Emerson, with her fierce appetite for knowledge, knew everything about being true to herself and never had a moment's thought about being brave. Can you understand then, Cecily, how being brave need not be a conscious act? When one is immersed in an honest life, there is no need to be brave for you are bravery itself.

Oh, isn't curiosity grand, Cecily! You and I would not know one another if we were not curious. You needed to know if flowers were truly medicine for a longing soul, and I – I allowed myself to fall under the spell you cast when you wrote and mailed that first letter.

A meeting at Helen's in the morning! Will the jumble sale provide enough money to restore the original tile roof on the old rectory? And if not, what shall plan "B" be? When the Village

Restorative meetings are at Helen's, we have full
attendance. Helen puts this down to her scones.

> Affectionately,
> Louise

> *Post Script.* I have never worn gloves.
> I accept this as a peculiarity of my own.
> A personal preference.

Rural Route 3, Box 549
Oakville, Washington
U. S. A.

Dear Mrs. Beauchamp,

My name is John Burrows, a friend of
Cecily Barnes. Miss Cecily tells me you're
having some trouble with caterpillars in
your fruit trees. I am a carpenter by trade,
Mrs. Beauchamp, and a self-made arborist
by nature. There is hardly a tree in all of
Oakville that I have not tended to at one time
or another, and none that I have not had the
pleasure of making the acquaintance of.

Now, I know my remedy to cause
havoc with the digestion of our American
caterpillars, but I cannot presume to know the
delicacy of your English caterpillar's digestion
and can only hope they share a common
dislike.

I am well prepared, though, to share with
you my unusual remedy for the removal of
pests from trees, which I derived from the
observation of a clothesline.

In the early summer of 1898, I stayed
with my sister and her family for a weekend.
I was strolling in her garden when I couldn't
help noticing her neighbor's most beautiful

orchard. I was leaning against the fence, admiring the wide variety of pear, apple, and plum trees, when her neighbor spotted me and, seeing my interest, took great pleasure in showing me around his much-loved orchard.

As we were making our way back, we were greeted by the sight of his wife taking down the day's wash from a clothesline strung between two apple trees. We chatted a few moments, and that was that. I gave no more thought to the matter until the following summer, whereupon another visit to my sister's home brought me again to the neighbor's fence. The devastation I saw caused my pipe to drop from my mouth – the once luscious orchard of fruit-bearing trees was hardly recognizable, so bad was the state of decay of the trees.

"Caterpillars," was all the man said, as he came and stood beside me. The scene was so startlingly different from the previous year in all aspects except one – the man's wife taking down the day's wash from the clothesline. My eyes ran along the clothesline to the two apple trees. Both trees were full of green, waxy leaves and succulent fruit.

"I can't figure it," the poor soul told me. "Those two apple trees are the only healthy

trees in the bunch, and I've cared for all my
trees in the same manner – smoke, salt, tar,
and lime."

Immediately I guessed the reason for
the two apple trees remaining healthy and
passed the idea on to the man, who after
reluctantly following my instructions, saw
great improvement and a healthy orchard the
next year.

It was the nails, Mrs. Beauchamp, the
nails fastening the clothesline to the trees.
You see, the sap intermingles with the cast
iron of the nails and produces ammonia. The
ammonia is then drawn upward with the sap
through the tree, and after being digested by
the caterpillar, causes its immediate demise.

I suggest hammering nails around the
base of your tree approximately a foot above
the ground. And use only headless nails, as
they cause less damage to the bark, which can
easily heal back over. If you have only a limb
or two infested with caterpillars, I suggest
inserting the nails directly below those
particular limbs.

To rid a tree of other insects, I often
give them a bath of either tobacco water or
a wash of lime. After scrubbing off the loose
bark from the tree, I wet it down completely;
this method does very well at destroying the

hiding places of insects. And if by chance
you have any decaying trees around, I would
see to it that they are destroyed, as they can
serve only too well as a nesting ground for
insects.

I hope I have not overdone it. I am hardly
ever asked about what I love so much. I adore
the tree in all its aspects and find myself
often stopping in mid-stride or mid-sentence
to observe a particular bend of a branch or
texture of bark or leaf. Friends indulge me
and let me ramble on, but I feel they are only
waiting for me to finish so we might again
take up 'more important conversation.'

I hope I have been of assistance.

Sincerely,
Mr. John Burrows

White Cottage
York Lane, Bishop Burton
Yorkshire, England

Dear Mr. Burrows,

I found your letter most interesting and went about acquiring nails the very next morning. Nails with no head are not to be found in our little village, so I laid the nails on a board and hammered the heads flat, until they no longer extended further outward than the nail.

In the past I have simply clipped infested branches from my trees. But this year so severe is the infestation that I would have nothing left but trunks!

I rather enjoyed your "over doing it," as you say. I am convinced if more people gave voice to what it is they adore rather than what they abhor, this would be a better world. When I am in the company (and I try hard not to be) of people who talk of nothing but criticism of this person or that or that condition or another, I find myself quite drained and am forced to retreat and restore my batteries with a rather large mounting of raspberry jam on a scone.

My dear friend Helen Curtis popped over while I was hammering the nails into my trees.

She thinks you must be quite brilliant. I told her I believe you are. I had made up my mind just before Helen arrived that I would send onto you my scone recipe. Scones are an all purpose remedy!

I mentioned this to Helen, me sending you my scone recipe. I could see she was thinking. After I had tapped a half dozen nails into my trees, she had not said a word, but I could tell she had something on her mind. I finally asked her. Her reply – "You're going to send Mr. Burrows your scone recipe then?"

"I'm not like you, Helen," I smiled. "I enjoy sharing my scone recipe."

"That's because it's the recipe on the bag of Be-Ro Self-Rising Flour. Everybody has it!"

"Not Mr. Burrows!" I said.

"I would think you'd want him to have the best scone recipe," was her reply. "He's saving your trees after all."

"But we all know that would be impossible, don't we, Helen? Everyone in Bishop Burton and the broader reaches of Yorkshire knows you keep that recipe under lock and key. I don't even have it." I added that, knowing full well what her reply was going to be.

"That's because you say you can't tell the difference between my scones and the scones from the Be-Ro recipe."

"That's true," I said, fully intending to keep my white lie.

45

"Well," Helen said, after watching me hammer in more nails, "I just thought you would have asked for my scone recipe to be sent to America."

I was speechless! I put the hammer down and just looked at her. It was Helen who finally spoke.

"Well, it wouldn't be likely anyone in England would see the recipe if we sent it to Mr. Burrows."

And then I understood! Helen wanted her scones to cross the Atlantic. She wanted their distinct and utterly delicious and unmistakable flavor to be tasted in America. I didn't make a fuss about it, I just told her to bring the recipe over in the next day or so and I would put it in my letter to you. So there you have it, Mr. Burrows, the elusive and exclusive Helen Curtis scone recipe. Enjoy!

Tell me, Mr. Burrows, on which side of the fence do you stand regarding Cecily's garden? If we are on the same side, might you put in a good word on Cecily's behalf to her father? So often a man hears best a voice spoken in the pitch and timbre similar to his own.

Most Respectfully,
Mrs. Louise Beauchamp

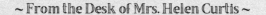

Recipe for Scones

2 cups flour
4 tsp baking powder
1 tbsp salt
6 tbsp cold butter
3 large eggs (save
   one for topping)

¾ cup milk
1 tsp vanilla extract
1 cup sugar (save ½ for topping)
½ cup currants
1 cup flour (for coating hands
   and working surface)

Mix flour and salt in basin and rub in butter (with fingers) until butter becomes small balls.

Add sugar and currants to the flour mix.

Push your hands into the mix and lift and let it sift through your fingers. Do this a dozen times. At least! (It adds air.)

Bring two eggs together with milk and whisk briskly for 3 minutes. No less. Add vanilla extract.

If you are wearing long sleeves, roll them up and secure them. Add wet ingredients to the dry ingredients. Powder your hands with flour and bring the wet and dry into a soft dough. Don't overwork it. Dust hands with flour whenever needed to prevent them sticking to the batter.

Turn the batter onto a flour-dusted surface and roll out to ¾ inch thickness. You can use a rolling pin or your hands to flatten down the soft dough. A secret to a good scone is a light hand.

Cut into 2½ inch rounds and put on a well-greased baking sheet. Whisk the egg and brush on top of the scones. Use the reserved ½ cup of sugar to sprinkle on the top, as you like.

Bake in a preheated 375° F oven for about 15-18 minutes. You are looking for a slightly more than golden color and the scones to be at least twice the height (or more) than they were before baking.

Rural Route 3, Box 549
Oakville, Washington
U. S. A.

Dear Mrs. Louise Beauchamp,

In answer to your question regarding
where I stand on Miss Cecily's behalf, my
answer comes without hesitation. I am in
complete favor of her garden – fence, tools,
and all. I see nothing wrong with a young
woman wanting a portion of the earth to seed
and call her own.
    The day after I helped Miss Cecily with
her fence, I arrived at the Barnes place
thinking I'd be finishing up my work on the
roof. But the professor was waiting for me
outside and said he had other work for me.
When he told me I was to take down Cecily's
garden fence, I told him I'd have nothing with
such nasty business and said I'd be on the
roof finishing up my job and would be gone
when I was done.
    I have always had the utmost respect for
the Professor, always found him to be a fair
man. I could not understand his behavior.
Why, I've seen him on an evening pause at
Cecily's garden, when she was not there,
taking in the beauty and breathing in its

fragrance.

I found more loose shingles on the roof, which forced me to return the very next day. I was bracing myself and was there for nearly a full hour before I let myself look over at Cecily's garden. Nothing had changed; our fence stood straight and strong as ever.

I almost dropped my hammer when the Professor called from below. He was in his buggy. I'm going into town, he said, need anything?

I assured him I had all I needed to finish the job. Well, thank you, he said. Thank you.

He's not a bad sort really. He is a bit barkish at times – crusty, if you know what I mean? I think he does his best at being both a mother and father to Miss Cecily.

Mrs. Beauchamp, please tell Mrs. Curtis that I am honored to have her scone recipe. I must admit it was a daunting prospect at first, attempting to create a Helen Curtis Scone, but I was determined and stuck with it. After the fifth attempt I knew I had something.

I sliced open a scone and buttered it. I refrained from the jam, as I wanted to experience the uninterrupted flavor of the scone, if you know what I mean. I had finished off three before I knew it. A scone is not a pastry and not a biscuit. It stands alone somewhere between, with its unique and pleasing taste and distinct texture.

The next day I baked a fresh batch and took them to a meeting of The Amateur Arborists Club. Not a crumb was left when the meeting was over, and by the end of the night I had standing orders for three batches of scones at a dozen each. I understand now why the envelope the recipe came in was secured with a wax seal. Along with the recipe was a note from Mrs. Curtis giving me full permission to share her recipe with whoever "seems like a respectable person." Better not think too hard about that one.

Please keep me informed about your caterpillar situation, and let me know if anything else should come up in which I might be of some help.

Yours Respectfully,
John Burrows

Cecily Barnes

Summer

Summer is the time for hammocks and lavender lemonade sipped in the shade. Have you, though, staked your holly-hock, delphinium, Canterbury bells, and other tall flowers? I have witnessed summer storms destroy unsupported tall flowers, leaving them helpless and broken. Prevention, as you've heard me preach for years, is the first and last word! As for roses, the romantics of our garden, frequent watering in the summer with a weak liquid manure is best, and don't turn your back on an aphid for a moment! They'll be sticking their sharp noses into your plants and sucking out their sap before you know they're even there! A spray of nicotine-sulphate and soap is best. If you see a single aphid, it means there are several hundreds in arm's reach, and beyond that, one can only surmise the legions and the horror of their destruction.

It is easy for an inexperienced gardener to become obsessed with insects and the horrifying mischief they are plotting day in and out and all night long amongst fragile petals and stems. Our helpless flowers bring us such sweet, selfless, graceful joy while asking only for a safe harbor in which to bloom. What if our flowers could cry out? An experienced gardener has a good grip on her emotions and imagination. But beginners, be aware – tender hearts make fertile soil!

Mrs. Louise Beauchamp
Newsletter ~ 22 June 1895

Rural Route 3, Box 542
Oakville, Washington
U.S.A.

Dear Louise,

All the flowers in my garden are bursting open and leaping into bloom! The picotee pinks and the golden banner coreopsis were first to bloom! Then the Shirley poppies and the larkspur followed. The hollyhock, foxglove, and delphinium reach to my waist!

I look forward to the arrival of your newsletters. I will take my time and read them slowly in the garden. I read all your letters in my garden. It is a habit I have developed, so that when a letter arrives there are no troubling, tumbling thoughts in my head; it is only you, me, and the garden.

A sow bug is a relative of the lobster? What is it doing here? How long ago did it crawl out of the sea and breathe air with its gills? Your letters fill me with so many delightful questions. I expanded my "Enemies of the Garden" chart to include your additions. Thank you for that. Have you always been this kind and interesting and generous? Are we like the flowers, Louise? Do we emerge from the seed and become what we already are? But how could this be? And yet, at the same time, how could this not be?

Oh, I must tell you the latest! Mr. Burrows brought over a dozen scones! I knew he had written to you with a remedy for the removal of caterpillars, but I never expected this! Mr. Burrows baking Helen Curtis' scones?

I made a pot of tea and we were sitting at the kitchen table when my father walked past in the hall. Mr. Burrows waved him over and said for him to join us. My father surprisingly accepted the invitation and was coming to join us when I noticed Mr. Burrows heaping a large helping of raspberry jam onto his scone.

We actually had a fine time. We were mostly eating. And when we weren't, we were discussing the fine features of Helen Curtis' scones and Mr. Burrows' surprising baking skills.

My father asks about you, and I tell him very little. I am keeping you all to myself. I do not wish to have a hard heart and see the practice of working in my garden as a spiritual ritual. Not to bring my father up again, his name is Arthur – though he doesn't look like an Arthur – he tells me that I potter around my garden as though I were an old woman! I think to myself, why is he talking about me like that? He doesn't even know me!

I have it in my mind to tell him that I can't wait to be an old woman potting about in a garden. That would really grind his oats! I could top it off with saying that one day I expect to hear the flowers talk. He'd be a real pot of oatmeal then!

You can see, Louise, what I am up against day in and day out. And then to top it off, after dinner this evening my father rose from the table, strode in front of the fireplace with his back stiff and his hands clenched behind his back. I have named this "Prime Lecture Position One." "P.L.P. One" for short.

I much prefer "P.L.P. Two," which is when he lights his pipe, puts his hands in his sweater pockets and leans against a doorframe. "P.L.P. One" is always the serious lecture. I don't know why he bothers, I really don't. It only ends with me getting a headache and him adding another wrinkle to his forehead. And he isn't getting any younger as it is.

My father informed me in this manner that Edmund Bentley would be joining us for dinner next Thursday. Thursdays are reward dinner nights. The students who score highest on my father's tests are invited; occasionally he invites a boy who is struggling, with the hope of encouraging him to try harder.

The boys who sit around my father's table on so many nights talk about the new century as though it were a ball in the palm of their hands to play with as they wish, while I am afraid of being smothered by what lies ahead or frightened I will be dragged along behind it. I resent their intellectual babbling. So inflated they are with dissected ideas that are not their own.

True conversation requires there be a listener as well as a speaker, but there are no listeners around that table. My father's students do not listen to one another – it is far too important to be heard. My father *hears them* but does not listen. He is thinking instead of how well they have retained what he has taught them during the year and what he might teach them the next. I listened in the beginning, but now I go away, sometimes in my mind and sometimes to the swing on the porch.

Edmund is my father's most prized student, and Edmund is very certain that he is more wonderful than all the rest. Then there is Rigor Thompson, my father's least talented student. I like Rigor the best because I understand his disappointment at never being heard.

My father thinks I ought to like Edmund. His family has lots of money. They live in a mansion. Really! A mansion. England has Windsor Castle. Oakville, Washington has the Bentley Mansion.

I want to tell my father if he thinks I ought to like Edmund Bentley then I think he ought to like Mrs. Percy. Mrs. Percy came to town a year ago with her little daughter, Annabelle. Mr. Percy was to follow, but so far he hasn't shown up – only shown up missing. Rumor has it there never was a Mr. Percy.

Mrs. Percy is my piano teacher, and I think she is lovely and smart and extremely accomplished and my father could do far worse. But I dare not cross that thin, inescapable line that divides us.

When I disagree with my father, he says it's because I am spoilt. If he knew of the low opinion I already have of myself, I am hopefully certain that he would not go on telling me such things.

My father has plans for me that keep me in continual motion when I so desperately need to be still. I will soon spill over and there will be no gathering me up after that.

I feel at odds with myself. Am I friend or foe? Why is it that while alone in the garden, I don't feel lonely, and yet when I'm in the company of others, I feel desperately adrift? I long for one thing in one moment and something else in the next. I am trying to sort out my emotions, but the more I try to untangle them, the tighter the knot becomes! The garden expects nothing from me, and I give it all I have. Others expect much of me and to them I give nothing if I can help it. I feel mean and dishonest, but to whom or what I do not know.

You said that I asked nothing from you but your seeds. Now you see that I am asking for more. I hope I am not burdening you with my problems. Know that I am grateful in the most immense way I know how to be grateful.

Your Dearest Flower,
Cecily

Post Script. I almost forgot – I must ask you about a plant I discovered growing quite rapidly in my garden and seemingly without any root at all. It looks as though it is a mass of fine yellow hair all gathered up and twisted. It has a pale white flower and bears no leaves. When I found it all bunched around my Margaret Pinks, I worked the entire morning pulling the bothersome thing away.

White Cottage
York Lane, Bishop Burton
Yorkshire, England

Dearest Cecily,

Dodder! Oh my dear, I pray I am wrong,
but from your description I am afraid it could be
nothing but dodder, one of the dreaded enemies
of our precious flowers. If it is dodder, and I do
so hope it is not, you will find what looks like
fine yellow hairs about an inch or two growing
in your garden or somewhere close about. Pluck
them out and leave no trace of root or blossom,
for this deadly enemy is strong and bent on
surviving and can thrive in any condition.

It begins as a fine single thread, at first
looking innocent enough. But then as soon as it
can stretch and reach another plant, it attaches
itself and lifts its roots from the ground, never
to return. It is a parasite and lives off the life of
other plants, sucking the juices from them until
they shrivel and die. The havoc dodder leaves in
its wake is of no concern to it as it moves on,
constantly looking for more helpless victims in
your garden.

I see this plant growing in its natural state on
high cliffs above the sea, looking quite pleasant

mixed together with other wild things. But in a garden, make no mistake, it is total destruction. Be quick about it, dear girl – don't wait another minute!

These feelings of meanness and dishonesty you speak of are just that – feelings. And although they feel very real, they are "real" only to the extent that they have gained your attention. Now we ask, what is it we are meant to see?

And please do not think you are burdening me with your problems. There is no higher esteemed virtue I value over trust, and you are trusting me with your heart. I am deeply honoured by this.

You have told me your father thinks you are spoilt. I don't believe you are spoilt, and if my instincts serve me right here, I don't think your father truly believes this himself.

I do, though, sense that you are lacking what you need for healthy growth. It is easy for one person to assume he knows what feeds the soul of another. The worst damage is often done with the best of intentions. Know this Cecily – no one possesses the potion for our happiness but ourselves. We need not put such an important matter in another's hands, when our own are quite capable of doing the job.

Growth has many stages. We do not always meet one another on the same path at the same time. Each cycle of growth causes the end of one phase and the beginning of another. Look at your flowers and ask yourself which phase of growth would you have them miss?

You wonder whether you are friend or foe. Indeed, this is a question we ask ourselves when we are, as you say, at odds with ourselves. We are both lovers of words, you and I. Copying out Emerson's Essays is a true act of admiration of the written word, and Mr. Emerson was a master. Now if we turn to those tangled and knotted thoughts of yours, you speak of feeling "mean" and "dishonest." Let me ask you this: what lies beneath these words? It is often the underside of a word that reveals what is waiting to be discovered.

We must learn to use the skill of judgment wisely. Discernment is necessary if we desire to be a kind and honest person, but when we judge ourselves too harshly we cause ourselves great harm. Could harsh self-judgment be the underside of the "meanness" you speak of? Just a thought.

Often, it is by entering into conversation with ourselves that we learn to hear the voices of others. Yes, even the voices of boys, even the Edmund Bentleys of the world, and if you can believe it, even the voices of fathers.

Regarding the wants of others, it is your business if you give or do not give what is asked of you. But I will tell you this – you must be honest in your giving. If not, you are dishonouring both yourself and the person to whom you have "given." I gave my seeds to you, not out of obligation or expectation, but because it felt good. So you see, Dearest Flower, by taking care of my own pleasures first, I took care of yours!

I will answer for you the question you asked: friend or foe. You are a friend to yourself. The best friend you have. We cannot give to others what we withhold from ourselves.

I'll be signing off now. My eyes aren't what they used to be. It's time for a good cup of tea and perhaps a delicious nap!

Affectionately,
Louise

Post Script. Back to the dodder. I hope I am wrong. Please let me know.

Rural Route 3, Box 542
Oakville, Washington
U.S.A.

Dear Louise,

My wise, wise dear Mrs. Louise Beauchamp, you are a gentle teacher. Have the delicate flowers taught you this? You instruct me to look and seek so that I might learn more about honesty.

I was surprised how quickly I recognized my judgment beneath the word "meanness." I at first felt great shame when I realized how I have judged others while being certain I was only observing them truly. But the shame did not stay; I sent it on its way with no judgment.

Oh, Louise, dodder it was. And I am saddened to say, it ravished my entire bed of asters and lavatera and all but one of my Iceland poppies. And even after all that, on the following Wednesday, I found my poor sunflower entirely covered with that horrid amber hair – all the way from its tall smooth stem to its beautiful face.

Mr. Burrows had been repairing fences for a farmer up the road and stopped by to pay a visit. We both worked at pulling the weed away. The more dodder we managed to untangle and separate from my sunflower, the more evident it was that the damage was too severe and that my dear sunflower could not survive in its weakened state.

I watched Mr. Burrows do what was necessary – burn my sunflower. It was the only way to save the others in the garden. My father came out, at first in alarm, and then seeing what we were doing, he stood back and said nothing. I did not let him see my tears.

Goodnight for now, my dear, dear Louise. I will continue my letter in the morning.

Dear Louise,

The morning came and went, and it is night again. I cannot say if I shall indeed send you this letter. I know only that I must write it. If I were to send this letter I would start with a question such as "when is the best time to water or to fertilize," but in my heart is only this one question: why is it that my mother died before I could remember her?

I was three years old when she died. Inside me there is an empty room where I believe the memory of her once lived. I wait in the hollow of that room for her memory to come back to me, but it does not.

My mother often walked in the field behind our house. I walk there and listen for her laughter in the dry rustling of the summer grass. I take walks along the river. I think that perhaps the river has held onto her reflection as she passed by this way, but it has not.

My mother's bed was brought out to the porch of our house so that her diseased lungs might better breathe the air. It was there she died. I often sit on the porch, on the swing there, and wonder how I might live.

Over the years, sometimes unexpectedly and sometimes predictably, my father has shared with me his memories of my mother. In the beginning I was too small to sit on the swing without sliding off, so my father would hold me in the crook of his left arm, my cheek resting against his white cotton shirt. In his right hand was his pipe. I remember imagining that the stories came from the pipe. The transparent swirls of white spiraled and twisted and then finally disappeared into the night and stayed hidden there until the next time my father breathed them into life.

It was a ritual and we both knew our parts by heart. Why did my mommy name me Cecily, I'd ask. He always considered this question as if hearing it for the first time. And in that magical silence, time spiraled backward.

"An angel came to your mother while she was sleeping," he'd say, "and the angel's name was Cecily." Then I'd eagerly add, "And the angel told mommy that she was going to have a little girl, and my mommy was so happy that she named me after the angel. Right?"

"Why, that's right," he'd say. And we'd sit there and swing slowly back and forth, listening to the crickets and the frogs. And then after just the right amount of time passed, I would ask, "How did mommy know the angel's name?"

My father would tuck his foot far beneath the swing, so that when he lifted it, we'd swing further than the circle of the lantern light, into the dark and then back again. Then he would draw in the fragrant smoke of his pipe and, lifting his head back, slowly blow it out, and I knew what was coming next.

"Why, angels have fine manners," he'd say. "I expect the angel introduced herself."

Manners are held in high regard in our home. I was glad of them; they were what held the napkins straight on our laps and kept the pleats in my favorite skirt. I'd snuggle deeper into my father's arms and feel the crispness of his well-mannered shirt against my cheek, and I would say, "Maybe the angel will come to me some day."

"Could be," he'd say, "could very well be." And off we'd go swinging into the night.

When I was eight, my father gave me geography lessons. The globe in his study and the piano in the parlor were our fondest possessions. So at the age of eight, I learned there were more people living in this world than I could imagine, and I asked my father how, with so many people in the world, did he ever find my mother?

I remember this story as a fairy tale. Though unlike the fairy tales I knew, the prince in this story was my father and the princess my mother.

Then last fall, when I'd been reading a school book for most of the evening and taking volumes of notes and going over again what I had read, checking and rechecking my notes, my father paused at the door of the dining room where I was studying. This must be an important test, he said, seeing that the table was full of opened books and scraps of crumpled papers thrown about.

It is, I replied. Continental Studies at eight in the morning.

He gazed at me a long while and started to walk away, then changed his mind. Your mother, he said, coming to the table and sitting down, his full coffee cup in his hand. She took the same class, the name was the same.

I closed the book, pushed away the stacks of notes, and leaned back in the chair. Is there another cup of that coffee? I asked. My father smiled, nodded, and fetched me a steaming mug. We both sipped, and let the warmth and aroma of the brew slow down time and make space.

"It was the winter of 1891," my father said. "My last year of college in Chicago. A popular philosopher was giving a public lecture on The Evolution of the Human Soul, and the hall was crammed full. I found a space against the back wall to lean against. It was then I saw her for the very first time."

"You told me that you met her in class," I said.

"Well," he said, "that was a smaller version. I think now you're old enough for the full story."

I felt my heart thump harder, and I sipped the hot coffee. Yes, I wanted to know more, I wanted the full story, but could my heart hold it? Of course, on the outside I let none of this be read from my face. My father put his mug down and gazed at a place just beyond me, and perhaps even beyond the walls of the house itself.

"She was seated in the front row," he said, "and she was wearing a pale pink dress. Her auburn hair was pinned up, and I could see her neck."

He blushed then and cleared his throat, but he did not put away the memories, and I knew he was there in that lecture hall, falling in love with the woman with a beautiful neck.

He said, "If she had turned around at that moment, I would have been able to tell you the color of her eyes and the way her left cheek dimpled when she smiled."

The lecture continued, and eight o'clock turned into nine and then ten. My father's eyes never strayed far from my mother.

"I waited where I was by the back door," he continued, his voice going back, back in time until I could hear the clatter of shoes on wooden floors and the excited voices of students who'd just heard a lecture they'd never forget.

My father smiled, remembering. "She went to the lectern and shook the professor's hand. I watched her head incline this way and that and her hands punctuate the air as she spoke. The professor threw back his head and laughed. Yes, I knew she would be brilliant, incapable of saying anything mundane." He smiled again, and I knew he was seeing her, watching her. I kept quiet, not wanting to send a ripple that might distort the clarity of his vision.

After a few moments he continued on. "When she finally made her way toward the back of the hall, she smiled at me. I was about to go up to her but she wasn't alone, she was with friends and was swept away with them.

"I'd never done anything like this before, but I was left with no choice. I could not let her go. I caught up with them as they were getting into a cab. I was breathless and when I tried to talk, the only thing that came out was a winded laugh.

"I must have looked like a silly fool, but I didn't care. I held out my hand to her and introduced myself. "Angela Wolff," she said, being a good sport and taking my hand."

My father moaned slightly and put his face in his hands, and I thought when he lifted his face, I would see tears. But instead he was stifling a laugh. "That's when I told the biggest, most whopping lie of my life."

"What did you say?" I asked, incredulous.

"I said: 'That was my brother lecturing back there. We're going for coffee. Would you like to come? He said he'd like that . . . if you wanted to come.' It was the first time in my life I had lied so blatantly while feeling so honest.

"She smiled and looked at her friends. They all shook their heads, saying there was that exam in Continental Studies at eight the next morning. All I knew was that I could not live the rest of my life knowing she was in this world and not with me. To my shock she said yes! I didn't know what I was going to do. I had no brother and even if I had, he certainly would not have been the man who delivered that unforgettable lecture."

"What happened?" I asked.

But he didn't hear me. He was lost then in the sweetness of his memories. I left him so that he might linger and that night might last.

My father completed his last year of college while my mother never began her second. Instead they married, and I was born the following year. A teaching position at a boys' academy in Washington State was offered to my father. They were both young and adventurous and going out west would be exciting!

My birth had not been an easy one, and my mother never gained her strength back. A persistent cough plagued her. They went to three different doctors. It was only after visiting the

71

fourth that they accepted that my mother was suffering from tuberculosis. My father begged her to go to the Sanatorium in eastern Washington State. But she could not bear to be separated from her husband and her baby. She said she could not imagine that being away from us would do anything but bring death closer.

This is where the porch comes in. It was summer and my father screened in the porch, and it was there he carried my mother and laid her on their bed that was placed there. She could breathe the fresh air that way. It would be good for her lungs. She would get better.

I think my father was certain that he loved my mother so much that when she took her last breath he would die with her. It doubtless came as a shock that he kept breathing after she stopped. I am certain he would give up every precious memory for just another moment with her. How unfair it is to have beyond our reach the only thing in our life worth reaching for.

Louise, I believe I am sick from a loss I can hardly remember but which sent down deep roots, so that wherever I look, there it is. When I watch my life from the outside I seem quite normal, even happy. But I live within myself, and it is there the sickness lies. And it is from there I cannot escape. No one knows I am sick. It is a secret I keep. I sometimes wonder if I might take this secret to my death.

I look at my mother's photograph and search

for her in the face of the woman whose eyes gaze only at the person taking her picture. I want her to look at me, to see me, so that I might see her. I have searched for her in my father's eyes but she is not there. We live in a house that is empty of her presence and full of her absence.

Lovingly,
Cecily

White Cottage
York Lane, Bishop Burton
Yorkshire, England

My Dearest Cecily,

I wish I could tell you that I understand why such things as your mother's death happen. But I too live with the mystery of such things. People, unlike trees and flowers, have seasons whose length cannot be known. What I can say to you, Cecily, is that I believe where there is love, there is light, even if that means one must go into the dark to find it.

Your father, I am certain, has suffered greatly. A parent wants to give his child all she needs. Your father cannot give you back your mother, and this must cause him immense grief. He has not only lost his beloved wife, but his daughter has lost her beloved mother. Twice then his heart has broken.

I am certain your mother must have loved you very much and would have wanted you to be happy, would have wanted to give you all the happiness she could. And though your mother is no longer with you, I do not believe she is lost. In a way that goes beyond explaining, I cannot help but think even now your joy is hers and your pain too.

We must be brave, Cecily, life accepts nothing less. And we are not without resources. We have our tools. We must look around for them and use them. There is always work to be done. Let the garden teach you its lessons.

Direct your tears to that place in your heart that is hard, so that it is able to grow soft, and to that place that is empty, so that it might become full.

There is always room for growth in the heart, as there is in the garden. But to acquire the space that is needed, we must discard what no longer serves the garden, what no longer serves us. To find out what this is often requires that we be still. And being still is the hardest work of all.

Think of the seed, Cecily, how it must be in the dark to open, enabling the shoot to sprout and roots to grow. It is only in stillness that new life takes root.

The garden is hard work, yes. But we do not cause the sun to shine nor the rain to fall; all this happens without any help from us. Often we are asked to give everything we have to the garden, and this at times can seem too much. But never does the garden ask for more than we are able to give.

Let go of expectations – they only build walls between what we long for and what is possible. So many times what is possible is so much more than we could ever expect.

And never be ashamed of your tears. Can you truly be so certain your father wouldn't understand? By assuming we know, unwittingly we prepare the way for the expected outcome.

Let the garden's beauty linger in your mind. Let possibilities take root and see what grows. Although we are an ocean apart, we have held the same seeds in our hands. We are not so far apart, you and I.

The enclosed drawing is of my own garden. I came across it the other day, and thought you might be interested. I feel we are walking the same path, walking through the same garden. I am further on than you, but in a way this world cannot explain, there is no distance between us. Grief has led us both to the garden.

Let me explain. I was twenty-three years old when my husband, at the age of twenty-seven, was killed in the outbreak of the Second Burmese War. In September of that same year, I gave birth to our stillborn daughter. My husband, Jules, never knew I was carrying our child.

After I buried my husband and then our daughter, I unraveled completely. There was nothing to anchor me down. A puff of wind could have blown me away. My parents insisted I move home with them. I tried but could not stay. I was a traveler in the world of grief, and all was foreign to me.

Life, though, struck a claim on me in the form of an extremely painful irritant in my left eye. A physician was called, and nothing could be found that explained the sharp, stabbing pain in my eye. I was invited by family friends to stay the winter with them in France. It was a relief for me, and I am certain for my parents, too, though they would never have admitted it. There was only pain in the house, with no remedy.

I sent a wire accepting the invitation and left the following week. I traveled first by steamer and then train. The rhythm of the train was soothing and carried me along, without any effort on my part, and this was a great comfort. I must have looked a fright in my black mourning dress with my pale face revealing itself in hesitant shadows from behind a veil.

Occasionally a fellow passenger would open the door to the compartment I traveled in, which was not a private compartment, and take one look at me, nod hello, and promptly close the door. Grief, some believe, is contagious. And so I traveled alone through Montereau, Troyes, Villeurbanne, and Cannes.

It was late afternoon when we reached the small town of Grasse. The train slowed as it wound its way round the sun-baked hills behind the Riviera, where the perfume industry of France grows fields of lavender. The train's steward opened my compartment door, and, assuming I was sleeping, moved quietly past me, gently slid open the window, and as quietly left.

What happened next is something I have told

no one, and even to myself, I have never tried to explain or understand it.

The warm Mediterranean sun released the heady fragrance of the lavender. The sweet breeze pressed against my veil, and then lifting it, brushed against my skin.

The sweet air intoxicated me – I will even say, took me over. I felt myself being dispersed and brought together as though I were a wave. Two waves, actually, one receding and one coming to shore. I turned to the open window and leaned out. My veil flew from me as my breath was pulled from my lungs. I fell back gasping. Then a sweetness beyond description wrapped around me, and for the first time since the deaths of my beloveds, I felt life stirring in me.

The irritant in my eye loosened and shifted across my vision, for a moment blurring and then bringing all into perfect focus. I blinked and a lavender seed fell into my open hand.

My surroundings rushed at me with a clarity I had never known before. I looked out the window and saw the world as fields and fields of lavender – braided they seemed, in tidy rows running up and down sloping, rolling hills.

The train began to slow, and I heard bells ringing out from a nearby abbey. I saw nuns, like ravens with wings fluttering, moving about in the fields of lavender. It was harvest time.

The train pulled into Grasse. I walked up the

hill to the abbey, and though I am not a Catholic, fell to my knees and prayed at the feet of Mary, Mother of Jesus.

I spent that night in the abbey with the nuns. We ate barley soup and bread and drank wonderful wine. A pretty rose-printed dress was found for me. It was never said, but I assumed it belonged to one of the nuns before she took her vows. It was a favorite dress, I could tell, with intricate lace at the neck and the wrists. They told me I was beautiful, and in their eyes, I saw my reflection. In their beauty, I saw my own, and I believed once again in all possibilities of life. I never reached my destination. Instead I met my destiny.

This, Cecily, is how I found my faith in the healing power of flowers and herbs. Fold this story away in your heart, away from the unbelieving hearts of others. It is not our work to convince others of miracles. It is enough that we believe in them – and live accordingly.

Affectionately,
Louise

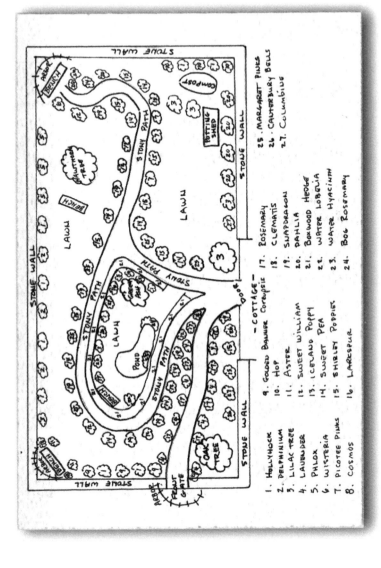

- COTTAGE -

1. HOLLYHOCK
2. DELPHINIUM
3. LILAC TREE
4. LAVENDER
5. PHLOX
6. WISTERIA
7. PICOTEE PINKS
8. COSMOS
9. GOLDEN BANNER COREOPSIS
10. HOP
11. ASTER
12. SWEET WILLIAM
13. ICELAND POPPY
14. SWEET PEA
15. SHIRLEY POPPIES
16. LARKSPUR
17. ROSEMARY
18. CLEMATIS
19. SNAPDRAGON
20. DAHLIA
21. BOXWOOD HEDGE
22. WATER LOBELIA
23. WATER HYACINTH
24. BOG ROSEMARY
25. MARGARET PINKS
26. CANTERBURY BELLS
27. COLUMBINE

Rural Route 3, Box 542
Oakville, Washington
U.S.A.

Dear Louise,

Thank you for your kind and dear letter. I have folded your story away in my heart, as you said I ought to. My heart is a bigger place now that your story is there. And it is not such a lonely place. The miracle of the lavender seed shall remain with me always, and my garden path shall curve and turn through the garden the same as yours. And when I walk on this path, I will know that I am not alone.

I have heard it said that when two souls wish for the same thing at the same time, that wish cannot help but come true. I believe it was destiny that put your seed catalogue into my hands and directed me to find you. I think we must have wished for one another. Or dare I imagine that you were sent to me, perhaps by my mother? I dare to believe such things that do not fit into the *normal* thoughts of my mind, when indeed I feel not normal at all.

Devotedly,
Cecily

White Cottage
York Lane, Bishop Burton
Yorkshire, England

Dearest Cecily,

To let in those thoughts that come to us from places which we cannot explain is both a daring and needful thing to do. What would we be if we only considered the known – only discovered what was already discovered? I do believe we must drop our buckets down deep into the wells of the unknown and then crank the handle and see what we have.

And do remember, Cecily, that because we have not yet a name for what we have, does not discount the validity of what we have. What we call the "unknown" might be quite well known in another land, or perhaps in another time than our own.

I believe our lives are so like the momentary scent of a flower; we are here on a thin wisp of air. Oh, but to be invited to such a party as is this life, Cecily, isn't it such an honour?

Louise

Rural Route 3, Box 542
Oakville, Washington
U.S.A.

Dearest Louise,

Perhaps this party is held in a house with many rooms, and I cannot think all at once of how happy I am that we two wandered into the same room and are now sitting across the same table from one another, looking at one another, seeing one another.

I do not believe there is an ocean between us, Mrs. Beauchamp. I believe only in the proximity of your spirit to mine. And my spirit reaches out to you. Sometimes I become afraid and think that my reach will not be sufficient, but always it is and always you are there. I sit in my garden and hear you humming; my own lips tickling as I hum along with you. My father would tell me it is the bees I am hearing, and I'd let him believe this is so.

> Always Lovingly,
> Cecily

Post Script. I believe the invitation to this "party of life" you speak of must have been whispered from the lips of angels.

83

Rural Route 3, Box 542
Oakville, Washington
U.S.A.

Dearest Louise,

It is late at this writing, and I can hear the call of the killdeer. It is a lonely sound. Or is it that the nighttime makes it seem that way?

This afternoon I mailed my letter to you. I cannot get it back to add more, so there is nothing to be done but write another letter. I don't think you'll mind. I am certain you won't. So dear have you become to me that I do not hesitate when I long to put down my feelings in words so you can hear my voice. My honest voice.

I imagine this letter arriving on the fall equinox. Will you and Mrs. Curtis and your neighboring pagans be brewing up something delightfully naughty? Although fall hasn't arrived yet, I can sense it is not far away; if it were a voice, I would say I hear it in the distance. The afternoons are sunny and warm but there is a knowing in the garden that a new season is nearing. Oh – and I have been meaning to tell you, Louise! The foxglove, delphinium, and hollyhock are now so tall that I am beginning to feel wonderfully small!

Your last letters (as your letters always do) give me much to think about. My father asks me what I think about while I am in my garden. I tell him I try not to think at all. He says I must be doing a good job of it then because I'm neglecting things that are important, such as acquiring oil for our lamps. He told me this while grading papers by candlelight.

I know life must have practicality, but if the light goes out in my heart, then there is no light. It is against this darkness that I work. Perhaps though, thinking now about something you wrote in an earlier letter, perhaps this is the darkness I must go into to find the light.

"Where there is love there is light," you wrote. "Even if that means we must go into the dark to find it." I must not forget this. But how does one know if it is the good dark or the bad dark?

I sometimes feel my father watching me from the house as I work in my garden. While turning over soil for new flowerbeds, I feel his disappointment in me break through the walls of our house, fly across the lawn, jump over my garden fence, and thump me on my back.

I do not let my father into this new world of mine. He does not fit. I feel terrible about saying that, and I will look closer into this matter of entering into conversation with myself "in order to hear the voice of others."

I am unable to find solace in sleep. I fear I know the cause of my affliction but not the remedy. This is why I am certain I must be spoilt. It was after dinner. I was putting in my time at the piano. My father was leaning against the fireplace mantle and smoking his pipe – P.L.P. Two ("Prime Lecturing Position," you may remember). I could feel his lightness of mood and this pleased me.

"Well," he said, when finally my half hour of torturing the piano was up. "You're making wonderful progress."

We both burst out laughing.

"Really," he said, "I mean it." But he could not keep a straight face, and again we were both laughing. In that moment, I was the little girl again on the swing held in my father's arms.

And then he said, "Cecily, it was supposed to be a surprise but I can't keep it to myself any longer. I'm going to bust if I don't tell you."

"What is it?" I asked, wiping away my tears of laughter.

"Mr. Burrow and Mr. Welks and myself have been planning your birthday party for over a month now. So far, half the town is coming, and we haven't even got all the invitations out yet!" I couldn't believe what I was hearing and the shock must have shown on my face because my father said.

"I've spoilt it for you. I should have kept it as a surprise."

"No," I said, "no, no, you haven't spoilt it."

I forced a smile and said how grateful I was
and explained that I was just very tired because
I hardly slept the night before. When I was
halfway up the stairs, I called down, "Goodnight."
I reached my bedroom, closed the door, and fell
onto my bed and cried into my pillow. I hear
the clock striking midnight now. I must tell you,
Louise: I am full of dread.

My worry comes from this: when at the
center of attention, I feel as though I am being
both looked at beneath a magnifying glass and
completely ignored all at the same time. I have no
idea what is expected of me, and at the end of
the evening, my cheeks hurt from keeping up an
untruthful smile.

There is more. I am convinced I stand before
the entire population of the room completely
undressed, so that all my soft parts are showing.
When I think logically, I know no one can really
see through my clothes. But while I am there,
surrounded by all those people, I cannot think
logically and am convinced I stand shamefully
before them all.

I cannot keep this suffering to myself any
longer and must tell someone. Who am I to trust
but you, Louise? And I am not entirely sure that
even you will not think I am suffering from lunacy
when I am so uncertain of it myself.

Oh Louise, it is my father who is an ocean
from me and not you. I wonder if my mother
were here, if she wouldn't fill that cold empty

space that is always present between my father and myself. There is so much space between us that often we cannot fit into the same room, and one of us is forced to leave so the other can breathe.

You have never seen me, Louise, yet you, like no other, look directly onto me and recognize me. And through your recognition I am fortified. I am being seen, and this assures me that I am here. That I take up space and might even possess a voice.

In your first letter to me you said I was either very beautiful or painfully plain. I can make myself look agreeable to an extent, I know, because after an hour in front of the mirror, I am told that I look pretty. But it is not me they are seeing as pretty but the face I have put on with powder and rouge. I have a small waist, but that is only after the torture of the corset. I do not wish to measure my worth by the size of my waist, but so often that seems to be the case.

It is in my plainness that I feel my self. My plainness is my clear pool of stillness, and I wish to live my life with this honest reflection of myself. I catch glimpses of this honest reflection but am not able to hold onto it.

Many times I feel empty in the company of others and seek out solitude. But then alone, with no one or nothing to distract me, I immediately fill the time doing one thing while thinking I ought to be doing another. And then when I force myself to be still, I am afraid I will disappear in the silence and solitude. The garden, though, is different; I mean, in the garden I feel as though I'm not alone.

Sometimes when on a solitary walk, I've felt as if a puff of wind could carry me off, so I've put pebbles in my pockets so I won't float away. Perhaps I am unearthing my life; the mess would make more sense if this were so.

But then I hear your voice reminding me that I must not let myself fall into the trap of limiting what makes sense to only what I *know* – I must go beyond what I know in order to know more. And be patient and not push to understand what I do not yet understand.

I will try to let go of the expectations of others without my reaching to pick them up before they hit the ground. "Fallen Expectations" – it sounds like a novel, don't you think?

I want to tell my father that I am not an old woman potting in my garden – though I think an old woman potting in her garden is charming, especially a bohemian English woman who lives in a charming English cottage and talks with flowers! I am a girl wanting to become a *woman*, not just a "bigger girl."

But I know he won't listen. Sometimes I think I will sink into the earth as silently as my mother did. Perhaps it will be then that he will hear me.

I do not talk about my mother to anyone. I don't think anyone wants to hear about your suffering when your suffering is supposed to be over. And besides, it is so hard to talk about someone you can only remember as a glimpse, as a shadow. This life does not measure things as they are; it only measures things as they seem.

I do not dare speak to anyone as openly as I write to you. Words written are so much braver than words spoken. Words written must be seen if one is to know what is being said. While words spoken can be heard and yet ignored. And this is the worst.

It is only with you, my dearest Louise, that I dare share what lies close to my heart. I fear if others read my thoughts that my feelings would be discredited. And then I, feeling ashamed of them, would abandon them and regret them, and for all my life be in search of them.

I saw Mrs. Percy in town today. I called out her name, but she did not hear me. And then I waved, but she did not see me.

It is only while in her house, sitting at the piano that she is vaguely aware of me. And to be honest, Louise, I am glad because I cause such horrid sounds to come from the piano she loves so much.

While she sits beside me during my lessons, I sense she is not there but somewhere else – somewhere full of lost things. I have dreamt about her many times, and always she appears atop a cliff looking down at a wild surf that crashes and breaks below.

White stock and white phlox are sending out their sweetness and luring moths into the garden. My window is open just a little, and the slight breeze floats my curtains, and then like a breath released, they fall again. A moth that was clinging to the curtain now flutters around my lamp as I write this letter. I find comfort in its small fluttering flight and believe somewhere deep inside that perhaps I could possibly possess the ability of flight. I wonder what my wings are made of.

Your Dearest Flower,
Cecily

Post Script. The flowers have not uttered a word.

Cecily Barnes

Fall

Every leaf remembers the tree. This thought drifted into my mind Tuesday afternoon last, as I watched a brisk wind pull off the last leaf from my apple tree. The leaf had caught my attention for a few days, as it seemed determined to stay on the branch. Then it was torn off and carried away over my garden wall. I had one last glimpse of it as it was swept up higher and then disappeared out of sight. I have enjoyed the thought of the leaves staying close to my trees, seeping back into the ground to rise up again through the tree and return in the spring as tree again. So it troubled me to think of the leaf being lost, lying somewhere in a ditch, not remembering the tree that grew it. I turned from the window, told myself it didn't matter, that it was only a leaf, that many thousands of leaves had left my garden in the same manner. But I had never witnessed the last leaf from a tree fall before; it was an entirely new experience for me. My nerves were still a bit jangled, I confess. And it was then the thought came to me – *every leaf remembers the tree.* I have learned over the years to respect a thought that doesn't pose a question but strides in bold as brass instead as a statement, without apologies or explanations. My nerves were soothed, and I went about the rest of my day in quiet solitude and satisfaction.

Mrs. Hall Watt is providing the refreshments for the annual bulb exchange; so don't eat anything for a fortnight prior to the meeting – you'll want to enjoy healthy portions of her steamed pudding and custard!

Mrs. Louise Beauchamp
Newsletter ~ 30 September 1902

White Cottage
York Lane, Bishop Burton
Yorkshire, England

Happy Birthday, Dearest Flower!

I've sent you an English birthday cracker.
It is the most popular party favour in England.
There is never a birthday party without a cracker
sitting beside each place setting. It takes two
people, each holding in their hands the ruffled
tissue paper ends of the little paper cylinder. You
twist and pull, and the smack of the little firework
inside will delight you, and then out will fall a
token – a fortune and a colorful tissue crown!
And there you have it – a perfect English birthday
party!

Dearest Cecily, know that your kingdom
reaches into the farthest realms of your soul.
Know that your kindness is your army; your
passion is your castle; and that you are both
humble servant and esteemed queen. There you
have it – my birthday wish for you!

Your letter did indeed arrive on the Autumnal
Equinox and found me and Mrs. Curtis, along with
pagan neighbors, going about all kinds of naughty
business – that consisted of some shared recipes

for squash soup. This ancient ritual took place in my garden around a pot of tea with Helen's scones and the pagans' homemade lemon curd. We lifted our finest china full of our black English Tea (with milk) and heralded the crossing of the sun over the celestial equator – that invisible line in the sky!

You said you were afraid if anyone else read your thoughts they would not understand your heart. It is here I must make a confession. Since your first letter arrived, I have shared every single one of them with Helen. We have laughed together and wept together over your letters. You see, I could not keep you all to myself. So now upon my confession, can you perhaps dare to believe there are others who will understand your heart and respect your feelings?

There was a time when I felt as though a puff of wind could carry me off as well. I imagined I was a rice paper kite with no tail or string to take hold of. It was very scary. But now I understand that to become one thing, we must first let go of another.

We could say the seed is broken, could we not? But you and I know better. We know the seed is not broken but is *open* and must open if the plant is to emerge, if the seed is to live with purpose – that is to say, to its full potential.

About your made-up face. The flowers will straighten you out on this one. They will show you their true faces, and you will not be able to look upon their natural beauty without revealing your own. The flowers will help you trust in who it is you feel yourself to be, which is often very different than what others expect.

Nurture your Self as you do your flowers, and you'll soon be rooted in the soil of your own being. The gardener, as your father has yet to understand, does not enter the garden to abandon the world but to see life close up. It is only by going inward that we can reach the stars and know them.

I have been thinking a lot about your fear of exposure, and let me tell you this: the feelings of invisibility and vulnerability of which you speak are quite common among women of all ages and bears no acquaintance with the tendencies of lunacy.

Women are told from the bellowings of society that by nature they are timid and weak. Nonsense, I say! By nature, which means in the natural state, women are immensely brave and strong. It is only when a woman is forced into the corset of a society that mistrusts her natural state that she loses her vigour and strength.

A woman's strength cannot truly be taken from her, for it is innate and inseparable from her being. But this is not to say that she might not forget this and then live as though she is powerless.

Do not believe for a moment that you are powerless. If you succumb to this false belief, then it shall be your own power that will destroy you. I do not mean to frighten you; I only want you to be aware.

In a "corseted society" that recognizes only rigidness and hardness as strength, a woman easily mistakes her softness for weakness and hardens her softness until she feels it no more. She interprets this non-feeling as strength and lives a life devoid of sensuality and honesty. If she continues on this way for too long, she will die, for a woman cannot live as a man. She must live as a woman and do the work of a woman. There is great honour in this.

It takes courage to go below the surface of life as you are doing and to explore greater depths "to find the measure of things as they are, not as they seem," as you say. This is a daring undertaking, but you are equal to it. To live an undiscovered life means that we can never take the first step into a stream or touch the first blossom of spring – never take the first bite of anything. An undiscovered life has been parceled and packaged for us by others. If we live in this way, we become disconnected from the source of all things, and soon we lose the curiosity to find things out – in essence, to take the journey of life for ourselves. We must be both the gardener and the guardian of our lives.

Know that you are brave – brave enough to find your voice, to stand by any words you write or say. We must be aware of fear, for like a weed in our garden, it is quite vigourous and wastes no time in putting down roots. Fear seeks us out at our most vulnerable hour, but it is in this same hour that we are presented with the greatest opportunity for growth.

And remember, dear Cecily, that weeds are truly orphaned flowers. If we embrace fear, sit it down and have a good conversation with it, it will take on an entirely useful place in our life.

In our bravest hour, fear is strength! Allow yourself to feel fear through and through, and then afterwards, wear it in your hair like the flower that it is. Remind yourself over and over that no one can take from you those things that grow in your heart.

Your Miss Percy is brave, is she not? She has stood her ground; she has not turned her face away in shame but has held her head high. And for this she has earned her reward, for what is more beautiful than being brave!

The garden is a place of constant change. Growth requires constant change. Yet the true self is firmly rooted, and regardless of change, we remain at the center eternally the same.

About good dark or bad dark? There is only dark – beyond this very simple fact, all other is point of view – personal speculation.

I hope you don't feel as though I've given you too harsh a raking-over, but I am certain we, like our garden soil, often need a good ruffling up to let some air in.

May all your birthdays be joyful celebrations of gratitude and kindness that you unwrap for yourself. You are in my thoughts as always, and as I have confessed, in Helen's thoughts as well.

Lovingly Always,
Louise

Post Script. Are you ready to hear
the voice of flowers?

White Cottage
York Lane, Bishop Burton
Yorkshire, England

Dearest Flower,

I have not heard from you and sense you are quiet, not in the way that quiet is a song, but in the way that quiet is sadness. There is nothing wrong with sadness. There are times when any other feeling would be dishonest.

I reread your letter, and the despair there frightens me.

I remind myself though that it is not only despair that I hear but also a new strength in you. You are knowing what you want! You say, you are a girl wanting to become a woman, not just a bigger girl. You are aware of the difference! I have seen many women stunted in growth, and for all their lives they remain the girl. They live an unscented life because they have never bloomed.

When I come upon such a woman I search out her eyes, so much I want to communicate with her soul and gently nudge her out of her little girl shoes. But one must be careful. You never know if her feet will come off with the shoes and then you have done her a grave disservice. (The path to hell is lined with good intentions). But you are a girl in search of the woman. This gives me great relief! And you imagine the possibility of flight and wonder what your wings are made of! Imagination always precedes invention. I expect you shall fashion your wings out of whatever your desire brings to you. Never, never underestimate the power of desire.

I'm certain you are just fine. Something must have come up, that is all. Something unexpected. There is always that chance that you wrote the letter, and it got lost in the post. This has been known to happen on rare occasions. So I will see you happy and being your lovely, curious self. Perhaps you have taken yourself for a walk and are discovering unexpected beauty never before imagined. I took myself on a short walk today, beyond my garden wall to the Yorkshire moors. I packed myself a little picnic. I was surrounded by lady's slipper, harebell, and golden rod. A thrush landed nearby to eat red bearberries. Soon we were joined by a magpie moth and a red-tailed humblebee. A flock of meadow brown butterflies flew by but did not stay. We spent nearly three quarters of an hour together, the four of us, and then we went our separate ways. But speaking for myself, I felt less alone than before, for instead of only me, I was also moth, bird, and bee.

> Hopefully Not Annoyingly,
> Louise

Post Script. If anyone tells you it's a shame that roses have thorns, ask them if they don't think it's wonderful that thorns have roses!

Rural Route 3, Box 542
Oakville, Washington
U.S.A.

My Dearest, Dearest Louise,

Your letter arrived the morning of my
birthday! Thank you so much for the birthday
cracker. It is so beautiful – too beautiful to break
open, so I have put it on my dresser where I can
admire it.

Well, are you ready to hear something
wonderful and amazing? I attended my birthday
party last night without wearing a corset!!!

Oh, you should have seen me, Louise. I
breathed fully and deeply, without restraint. And
you should have seen me dance, too. I was the
center of my party and did not mind! I do not
understand the strangeness of this world, for
although I was less clothed than before, I felt less
vulnerable. I shall never again wear a corset!

And Louise . . . I have met a young man.
He came to my party with one of my father's
students. His name is Quentin Lawrence. What
a nice name, don't you think? Sounds like a
flower – a rather noble, stately flower with
gentle petals. He is from Chehalis, a small town
east of us. When he graduates from high school,

he will attend Agriculture College in Seattle.

He hasn't quoted Sir Francis Bacon, and he has never heard even heard of Lucretius. He can't dance very well but I don't mind. He has very nice hands. I showed him around my garden, and he asked about my soil! Never have any of my father's students asked about what is important to me!

Quentin said our immigrant garden was the most beautiful he has ever seen. I told him all about you. And he said you must be a kind and sincere woman, and I said, oh yes she is, she is all the best I hope to be. And then I was going to tell him that you carried on lengthy conversations with flowers, but I didn't want him thinking you odd, so I said instead that you were a wonderful conversationalist. And he said that he thought as much, considering the way you write wonderful letters. I haven't let Quentin read your letters. I have only told him about them. Oh, but Louise, know that I am not in the least bit upset that you have, since the beginning, shared my letters with Helen. I see this as a great honor. I feel doubly blessed now!

Quentin and I go for walks in the country, and he tells me about the trees we pass, whether they are wind pollinated or pollinated by bees and insects. I have never found trees so fascinating before. We read to one another in the afternoon from your mother's Emerson. Oh and Louise, the lobe of his ear is soft like lamb's ear.

Dearest Louise,

I have taken up my pen again. I cannot believe nearly a week has passed since I began this letter. You must wonder what is going on with me! I'm sorry if I've worried you. I must have worried you after the letter I wrote that night my father broke the news about my birthday party. But so much has changed since then!

The day after my birthday, it rained the entire day, and Quentin and I spent the whole afternoon on the porch swing, taking in the beauty of the flowers. It was a soft summer rain, and the garden seemed soothed by it.

I was thinking of this when Quentin said, "Cecily, if you'd like, I could make you a fine swing for your garden. I could even put a roof over it so you'd stay dry in the rain."

Louise, he has gentle brown eyes that smile when he does. I only dare hold his gaze for the count of three! I am certain I went over my limit this time.

I shot up from the swing under the pretense of getting a better look at where such a swing might be placed in my garden. Quentin started building the swing the very next day.

My father did not like this one little bit, which is the most I will tell you about what he said, except for one thing. I must tell you this one thing. As he walked away, he said over his shoulder, "He'd better not be expecting to use any of my tools."

Then listen to this! That very same evening my father said we ought to invite Quentin to dinner sometime. This is the real punch – he expected I would agree to have Quentin be joined by Edmund and a few other boys from father's classes. I said absolutely not! Not in a million years!

My father cleared his throat, one of his habitual mannerisms when things get off track. He attempts to get them back on track by clearing his throat. I've never seen it work but thought I might as well give it a try myself. When I cleared my throat in the same manner, he shot me a look of daggers from across the room!

I was confident I'd gotten my point across and thought I'd better not push it further. So I added that I could bake pork chops with stuffing when Quentin came for dinner. I know this to be my father's favorite meal. This took the edge off.

Yesterday Quentin finished the swing and stayed for Sunday dinner. I listened but heard no conversation coming from either of them while I was seeing to the pork chops in the kitchen. Then I heard wisps of words now and then about rain and the lack of it for this time of year compared with other times of year.

Oh Louise, I wish you could have been at the dinner table with us. It was poetry, complete poetry. My father asked Quentin what he intended to do after he left school. Go on to an Ivy League college?

"I'm going to be a farmer," Quentin said.

"A farmer," my father repeated and went on asking Quentin if he didn't want to go on to get a degree in business or perhaps law. Quentin smiled (and you should see his smile!) and asked my father if he'd ever smelled a freshly plowed field after a rain.

My father was thinking if he had or not when Quentin went on, "It's the best smell in the world. And have you ever been out farming before the sun comes up, so that when it does come up, you're sure you're the first person in the world to see it?"

My father didn't suspect such boldness. He shifted in his chair and cleared his throat, his gaze never leaving Quentin.

"I can't explain it, Mr. Barnes," Quentin went on. "I'm not good with words. All I know is, it's when I'm out in the field that I know anything for sure.

"And what is it you know for sure?" my father asked, suspiciously.

"I know that if I take care of the field, the field will take care of me." You could have blown my father over with a feather.

As for me, well, I wasn't surprised. Just delighted to sit at our dining table and hear for the first time original thought served up so eloquently.

My father took himself off to his study, saying he had some papers to grade. Quentin and I took our dessert out to the garden. The flowers are so beautiful, and I show them off every chance I get.

Dearest Louise, over and over again I am reminded of your purest goodness. You have given me your garden and your wisdom, and often I cannot contain my gratitude and find myself crying as I touch a delicate flower or tender shoot. More than anything, your flowers are teaching me compassion. I cannot explain it, it just appears so. I feel as though I am a different being, or perhaps I am realizing that which I have been all along.

But now I am philosophizing, and that is something I only do with you, Mrs. Beauchamp, my dearest, dearest Mrs. Louise Beauchamp of White Cottage, Yorkshire England.

Always Your Dearest Flower,
Cecily

Post Script. And yes, I am ready to hear the voice of flowers.

October 31, 1910

AUSTRALIA, WASH.
NOV 1
1910

POST CARD

THIS SIDE FOR THE ADDRESS ONLY

THIS SPACE MAY BE USED FOR WRITING

My Dearest, Dear Louise
I am so sorry to have worried
you. I did not mail my letter til
the 10th! So carried away. I
have been with all the glorious
changes in my life! You will Know
all about them by now! I see
you so clearly on your picnic
with bird, moth and bee.
This afternoon we went on
a picnic, Quentin and I
Never again shall I underestimate   the Power of desire!

Mrs. Louise Beauchamp
York LANE
Bishop Burton
Yorkshire

ENGLAND

Always Lovingly, Cecily

109

White Cottage
York Lane, Bishop Burton
Yorkshire, England

Dearest Flower,

You indeed flatter me, and I must say I am becoming quite used to it; that is to say, I like it very much. With all my gardening through the years, I could not imagine a blossom as wonderful as you, Cecily.

And do know, my dear, that because you have unbound yourself from the corset, I too breathe easier. You have reached a new world, Cecily, and there will be much to be discovered!

I have, though, been thinking about your father and your unhappiness with him. Loving fathers are not always able to express their love in the way their daughters desire it to be expressed – the words aren't right, the timing wrong, the gestures awkward – so much left to interpretation. Fathers are so often like deep rivers, obscure at first, but after a longer gaze, the depths reveal themselves. I will go further and say that this river longs for the reflection of the daughter – longs to be seen past the shadows and into the heart.

I have a theory that rivers in general troll for troubled souls, which is why, often, after spending time beside a river, we are left feeling lighter than before, less burdened – without quite knowing why.

It has been rain off and on all day, with delightful visits from the sun. Now a fine autumn night has settled in, with the crispness of winter brushing my cheeks. Winter will be coming soon, and you'll need to harvest seeds and winterize your garden. I think you have similar winters to us in this part of England, so here are some suggestions for you. Rake dry leaves over all your perennials. Hold the leaves down with evergreen boughs, making sure you are not crushing the plant. Be careful not to do this when temperatures can still rise. If this is done too early, the heat from the sun can swell the buds on the plant, and then when the cold comes they will freeze, perhaps even killing the entire plant. When spring comes, remove the boughs and leaves gradually. Your grass is a good guide. When you see new grass growing in the fields and lawns, that's the time to slowly remove the winter mulch.

I have found it helpful to cover my propagating frame with shutters to keep out the cold. Because I use coal to heat the cottage, I have plenty of coal ashes. I mix them together with finely chopped straw, and it makes a wonderful, rich mulch.

I am sending you some gardening books I have collected over the years. I think you will find them useful. I have spent many contented winter afternoons with them spread out on the hearthrug, contemplating my spring plantings.

Always Your Dearest,
Louise

Rural Route 3, Box 542
Oakville, Washington
U.S.A.

My Dearest Louise,

I have harvested the first seeds from our
immigrant garden! I spent the entire week
packaging and labeling the seeds. Dare I say,
I found myself feeling a little like you, Louise?
I am so grateful that after being thoroughly
finished with the seed business, you found it
in your heart to send out your seeds one last
time, and that I was the blessed one to receive
them.

Per your instructions my garden will be well
protected through the winter months. Shutters
for the propagating frame is a wonderful idea.
My garden is quiet, except for the lavender and
a second bloom of delphinium. I think of the
garden as myself now, such as when I am quiet,
it is because I feel satisfied with silence. Silence
is no longer loneliness, silence is full of space.
And I cannot imagine ever not living in such
purity of space as exists in the garden – in my
mind, in my soul.

I have found though, when I am not satisfied, I cannot keep the silence. The silence instead becomes my force and empowers me to speak. Such was the situation this Tuesday past. I told my father I was going to ask Mr. Welks if he would be interested in hiring me on as a clerk. I know he could use some help, and I would not take much in the way of pay, just a little so I can have a bit of money of my own.

My father told me it wouldn't be possible for Mr. Welks to hire me because I am white and Mr. Welks is black. He asked me please not to put Mr. Welks in an embarrassing situation.

I went straight away to the dry goods store and asked for a job. Mr. Welks echoed my father's very words. Where have I been all this time? How have I not been aware of this injustice? Though, at the end of my father's words, Mr. Welks added a few of his own. He said, "You nor I made the world as it is. We just got to live in it."

I told him we ought to change the world then, that it is not acceptable the way it is. He was pushing his broom past the flour bins (he does this more than a dozen times in one day – he likes his floors clean). He paused, as though collecting his thoughts. But when he spoke, I realized he must have had second thoughts and let the first ones go, because all he said was, "Sorry."

My heart is not white or black. It is a human heart that beats the same as that of any other heart. As I write this, my heart aches for my dear friend, Mr. Rufus T. Welks. A finer friend you could not wish to have. He knows no strangers; all he meets are friends he's yet to make the acquaintance of.

There is a revolution coming to the state of Washington. I have joined the suffrage marches. It is time women become enfranchised; it is time women had their voices heard and are able to cast a vote so the laws that govern them might also represent them.

On a lighter note – your gardening books arrived in the afternoon post! Mr. Welks brought them over himself on his way home. (Though we live on the west edge of town and he the east!) Normally he lets the afternoon post get picked up the next morning, but he wanted me to have your package as soon as possible, and he knew I'd most likely be waiting for it.

Kindness must be the dearest of all dear things. I believe you and Mr. Welks would get along quite wonderfully. You share so many of the same attributes that I respect so much.

I have the box open before me as I write this! I know that you are giving me your books because it pleases you to do so, and by you following your desire, you are fulfilling mine!

(I *am* learning.) We are both blessed, but me, believe me, more so! Tell Helen hello from me!

> Your Dearest Flower,
> Cecily

Post Script. Find enclosed a photograph of Quentin and me in the garden. Notice the hollyhocks behind us? Nine and a half feet tall and no rust!

White Cottage
York Lane, Bishop Burton
Yorkshire, England

Dearest Cecily,

Thank you for the photograph of you and
your Mr. Quentin Lawrence. You are a very
handsome pair. I'm so glad of your happiness.
I must tell you about a garden I visited in
Chelsea some years back. Everything planted in
this garden was pink! Pink mallow, pink dahlias,
pink sweet peas, pink Sweet William – I could
go on, but do not wish to recreate such a horrid
image in my mind.
Well, it's there in my mind now, and I can
tell you with renewed clarity the horror of it. The
poor flowers were deprived of anything but pink
conversations! "How are you today?" "Oh, very
pink. How about you?" "Pink, as usual."
Think of it! Nothing to discuss! I tell you,
Cecily, I could see plainly in the faces of the
flowers their deprivation.
This happened on a cycling trip with some
ladies from the garden club, and the address
was given to us as a point of an afternoon
cycling destination. Well, when tea was served
in the house, I lingered in the garden alone for

a few minutes. And just as I suspected, the poor darlings couldn't wait to spill their despair to someone who might listen. I listened without saying a word; they had a lot to get off their chests.

While on cycling outings, I am in the habit of carrying wildflower seeds of a wide variety in my pockets to toss about on the roadside. The country lane we cycled on this outing was free of hills, so we did not take any rests, which is always an opportune time for me to do a little "on the road gardening." And the pink monstrosity was our destination, so we did not picnic. Which meant that I had my full load of seeds.

You can imagine the sighs of relief, Cecily, when I dispersed my ample supply of wildflower seeds in that poor garden. I have taken delight in imagining the expression on Mrs. Horton Green's face when that next spring purple lady's smock popped up, and deep blue flame creeper and red candytuft, to mention just a few. A good deed like that can float one for months!

When one is a gardener, one must take seriously into account the conversation various flowers are able to share with one another. After all, a garden is a community, and flowers do become quite fond of one another. A garden is about growth, and where is growth without good conversation?

I did hear mention that a Mrs. Horton Greene of Chelsea removed her name from the garden tour registry. Not to say it is good to judge anyone, Cecily, but if you are forced into the predicament of having to do so for one good reason or another, the quickest and surest way is to look at their garden. One need not go through their front door to know what they have in their wardrobes.

The world, as well as the garden, prospers from diversity and variety. This world we live in would be a dull place indeed if we were all alike. I believe it is the difference in each that brings out the best in the other.

Please send my best wishes to your friend, Mr. Rufus T. Welks. Tell him an old woman in Yorkshire, England thanks him for carrying her flower packets so that Miss Cecily Barnes was able to find her.

How ever in the beginning men thought a woman did not have the right to cast a vote is beyond me. We on this side of the Atlantic are fighting for the same rights. Equality among all is what I say. And the men I converse with feel the same way I do.

In the papers just last week, I read where a woman was arrested for throwing a rock through the window of the House of Commons in protest. And a friend of the same woman put paste down a pillar box, causing all the mail to be sticky. It gummed up the works indeed.

A woman's voice can travel far when she decides to use it. Who else would know better than a woman where her place is? Not all women have to agree, but those who do not possess political minds ought not to obstruct the way of those women who do. I am on your side, Dearest Flower, although I am over here!

Now here is some news for you. While you are preparing your garden for the winter, I will be traveling to Italy. My physician insists the warmer climate suits my condition. He is an old friend and a relentless old fool – no doubt too old to be practicing medicine. But I have learned to yield if I am to have any peace from the man.

The medicine is not so bad. I will be staying with young friends in Tuscany for a few weeks. (I've been instructed by my doctor to stay the entire winter, whereas I insist a few weeks will do me nicely.) My friends are the sixth generation of the Angotti family to live in this beautiful villa that was once an abbey. The many terraces look out on an olive grove, and beyond that are cypress trees and the beautiful rolling hills of Tuscany. And of course, the warming sun and the delightful villagers.

I do so like Italy, but I do so dislike leaving my garden. My Tuscany friends understand this, and while I am there, I am treated to pots of blooming lavender filling the windows in my rooms.

I will send you a postcard from Italy! And

on my journey home I shall be thinking fondly
of the letter from you waiting for me.

Always Lovingly,
Louise

My Dear Cecily,

    I am being treated like the Queen Mother over here! I hope you enjoy the picture on this card. It is just as magical as it looks! The children of the house are delightful, and all three of them play the mandolin. Charming little concerts each night after dinner. I am feeling much better and will be arriving home in early January.

Lovingly, Your Dear Louise

Rural Route 3, Box 542
Oakville, Washington
U.S.A.

My Dearest Louise,

Here is your letter waiting for you! I was happy to receive your postcard and am so glad your health is restored. The Tuscany villa looks enchanting. I cannot imagine being in such a place! Do take care of yourself.

By the time you read this, we shall be in the New Year. Per your instructions, I have mulched my perennials and my annual beds. I scattered well-raked barn manure lightly over the perennials and more heavily over the hollyhocks. And I did remember to lay branches over the plants first, so that they might not be suffocated by what it is that will sustain them through the winter. Isn't it interesting Louise, that what nurtures a flower can also suffocate it? I understand more and more how there is not so much difference between people and flowers. On the rest of the garden I have put dried leaves and boughs. In the dark, dreary days of winter I shall be cheered by the magic in my garden that is lying in wait for spring!

I have been spending time beside the fire

looking through your gardening books, and I must admit, when I found your first notation in a margin, I went through all the books looking for them. I see them as notes to me, that even then, when you didn't know me, you were sending me messages.

I have passed on your kind regards to Mr. Welks. He said you and I must be getting to know one another pretty well by now. I said we are indeed.

After Christmas dinner, I played Bach's Prelude in C Major for Quentin and my father. I love the piece and never believed I would be able to play such a beautiful piece of music and have it sound beautiful! Bach would not have minded, and Quentin and my father enjoyed it immensely, and I so love playing for them. I pleased myself and in doing so pleased them as well!

I have told Miss Percy about you and me. She believes it was destiny that put your seed catalogue in my hand that day at Mr. Welk's store. She said that you and I must have wished for each other. Miss Percy regards highly the spiritual matters of life.

Last week after my piano lesson, Miss Percy and I took a walk. Behind her house is a beautiful little river that runs through a field. We strolled along its bank with the afternoon sun warming our faces and throwing sparkles on the river.

I told her that when I'm playing the piano, the notes don't make sense. She said it was the silences that make the music, not the notes – that the notes would spill away if it were not for the silences holding them in place.

I couldn't wait to share this with you!

I told her that one day I hope to make something of myself. She said life sometimes demands that we stay still and that it's up to us to find where we belong and then claim it. She said we don't create anything, we discover and arrange, and in this way we touch the divine, and how much closer to God can you get than that?

I think you would like Isabella Percy, Louise. I believe she is the most beautiful woman I know, second to you.

Now, My Dearest Louise, I have some news for you. I have decided we must finally meet. I shall come to England in the spring! We shall spend our mornings in your sitting room beside the fire and not stop talking the whole time. And then in the afternoons, we shall linger in the garden and watch the first blooms of spring, and I will meet the ancestors of my flowers.

Every night I have prayed that Providence shall lay before my eyes the means by which I shall acquire such funds, and now it has happened! A Mr. and Mrs. Floyd Parker are traveling to England in the spring with their young children and wish to have a nanny accompany them! I answered the advertisement last week, and today received the news! England in the spring!

I have no doubt, Louise, that I shall come

to your wonderful country, walk through your garden gate, and stand at your cottage door. In my imagination I am already there.

Lovingly, Impatiently,
Your Dearest Flower

Post Script. I heard a whisper from the garden.

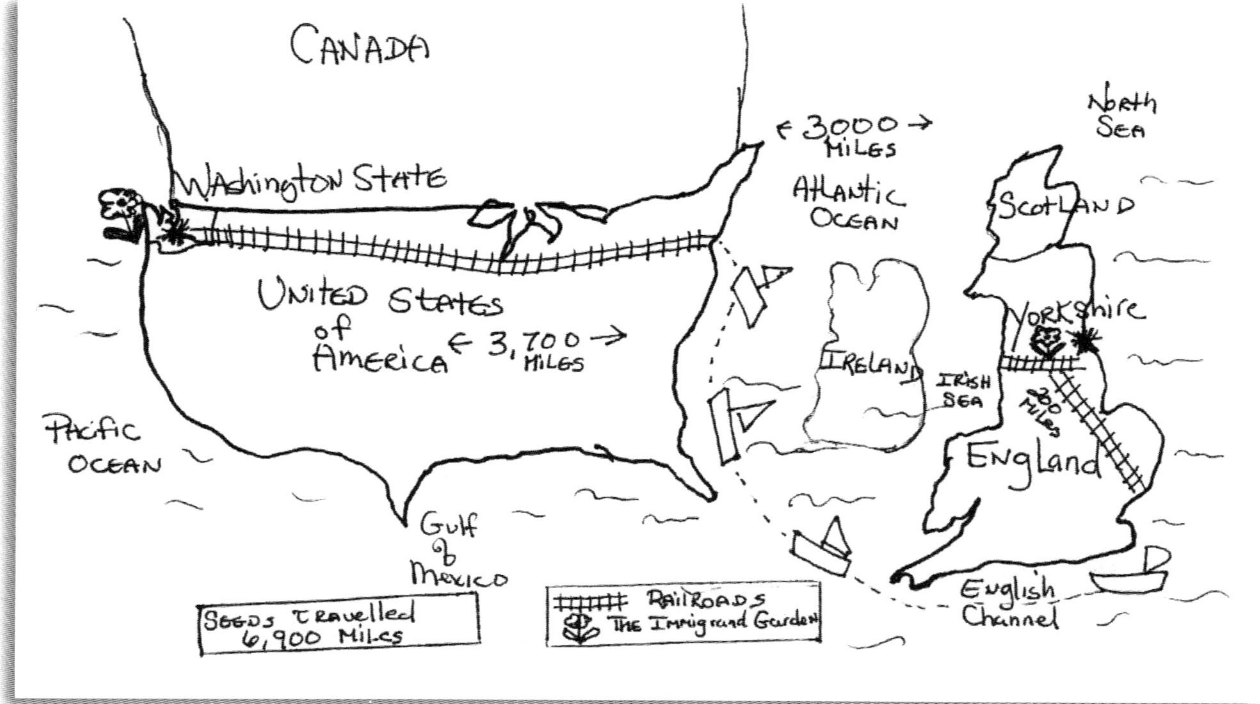
CANADA
Washington State
United States of America
← 3,700 → Miles
Pacific Ocean
Gulf of Mexico
← 3000 → Miles
Atlantic Ocean
Ireland
Irish Sea
Scotland
North Sea
Yorkshire
200 Miles
England
English Channel
Seeds Travelled 6,900 Miles
Railroads
The Immigrant Garden

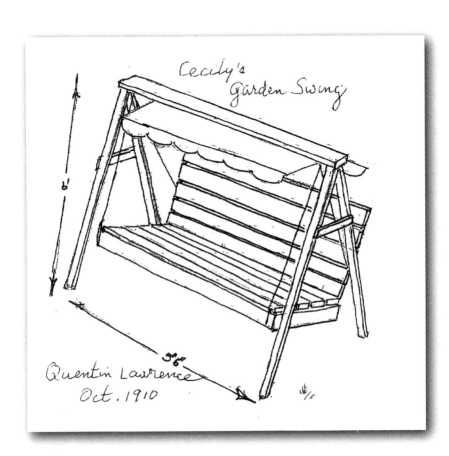

Cecily's
Garden Swing

6'

5'6"

Quentin Lawrence
Oct. 1910

Winter

Winter does not end the music in the garden but instead lowers the volume that we might hear the subtler music – the aboriginal notes if you will – those ancient songs that have woven and threaded through leaf, blossom, stem, and stalk from time's beginning.

How is this done you might wonder? How does one "hear" such music from so long ago? We must let the garden shed its garments so that what is left is the essence of the shrub, tree, and plant. In this state the winter garden will reveal its original music. Bare, intricate sweeping branches are the fine bows that vibrate ethereal strings. Listen and you will hear, bend low and you shall be lifted up, reach out and you shall be touched. These are the lyrics played on a winter's day, when the air is crisp and the sky blue and the garden is held in eloquent silhouette.

Winter adorns the humblest thicket with her most precious jewels. Winterberry, bayberry, hawthorn, vaccinium, and malus are especially beautiful in winter. If any of you are in need of extra birdseed, Harry Picket has more than he needs and will have an ample amount available at the next meeting – which will be held at his home at the regular time. Mrs. Curtis is providing the refreshments.

Mrs. Louise Beauchamp
Newsletter ~ 5 January 1884

Cecily Barnes

White Cottage
York Lane, Bishop Burton
Yorkshire, England

Dearest Cecily,

Oh yes, come, my child! I have plenty of
room, especially in my heart. After reading your
letter, I went out to the garden and spread the
news to the flowers about your coming.

Oh, it is good to be home in my little cottage.
There is no snow on the ground, and the days
are unseasonably mild. Though after Italy, I must
confess it does seem a bit nippy.

I spend most of my time indoors beside
the fire, working on my embroidery. I have
grown quite old these days. I don't know how
it happened. I was keeping such a good eye on
my garden gate. But Old Age tapped me on the
shoulder while I was busy with my flowers and
announced she was moving in. I did grumble at
first, but now Old Age and I spend entire days in
my little sitting room enjoying our own company.

My flowers are not happy about this
arrangement. Weeds, those dear orphaned
flowers, are finding their way into the garden.
I had to remind some of the flowers that in the
beginning I collected seeds from the field and

131

various other places and brought them into the garden. They have forgotten this and believe they have always lived in the world they know enclosed by the garden wall.

My eyes are not what they once were, so Helen reads aloud to me your letters from the beginning. We always start at the beginning.

Bach's Prelude in C Major is one of my favorites, and now when I hum it, I hear you at your piano. I'm so happy that you are now enjoying your lessons. Isabella Percy is surely a remarkable person, and she must be very pleased with your progress. I feel you and she are growing a deeper friendship.

My mind travels often to you and your father. And I think about my own father. We sat outside one summer night, and we looked up at the stars. He said, "It makes you wonder, doesn't it?" My father worked long hours in the fields, and when he came home, he was tired. His hands were thick and full of callouses. I sat beside him, and instead of looking at the stars, I looked at him and was full of wonder. I wondered who he was. I wondered what to say to him. We'd never talked about the mystery of the stars before.

He died soon after that. I was just getting to know him. I did not know that time was short and that even waiting a day would be too long.

I don't think my father was ever aware of how much I cared about what he thought. His thoughts were selfless thoughts, while mine were only full of myself. My father began pulling away from me; he stopped listening to me, stopped seeking me out – or so I thought. Until I realized, it was I who had gone away, I who had stopped listening, I who had stopped seeking him.

It is too late for my father and me. I suppose this is why I linger on the image of you and your father in the garden.

I have a miniature portrait of my father. He was a blonde little boy with a round face and serious eyes. This little boy became my father; this little boy must have always been somewhere in my father. The questions I would have asked him are many; the ways I could have known him are numberless.

The garden was the place my father and I could have met but did not. The garden is young again, as it was then, and I like to imagine there could still be time.

With all his misunderstanding, I am certain your father loves you. And you, Dearest Flower, still have him. But this is really none of my business, and you must make the choices that are best for you.

I awake early these mornings, before the sun, before I hear the neighbor's rooster. I hardly sleep deep these days. Instead, I skim on the surface of sleep like a damselfly across a pond. Often in the slow light of early morning, my eyes study the landscapes that reveal themselves on the back of my hands. I am becoming transparent, you see –

so that veins have become winding rivers running across the cracked desert of the back of my hand. It appears to me that I am becoming part of everything else. You name it – a fleeting cloud, a blade of grass, the colour of red in a cardigan. The sound of water running in my little brook, a single leaf on a tree, a curve in a country lane – the line of separation is erasing. It is hardly there at all any more.

On early mornings I often find myself in that place between wakefulness and sleep – between two shores, if you will. I rise and fall on the gentle waves there and wake to the scent of ocean in my hair. You see, Dearest Flower – I am a dreamer even while dreaming.

I look forward to your visit in the spring. Helen and I are busy making plans. You must see York and of course Stratford-on-Avon.

> Affectionately, and as
> you say, Impatiently,
> Louise

Post Script. So, you are hearing whispers from your garden. The time must be near.

Rural Route 3, Box 542
Oakville, Washington
U.S.A.

My Dearest Louise,

Your flowers are expecting me! And oh how I already adore them – even know them! I shall tell them all about their first American generation! Oh, I will say, they are a wild bunch, and there is nothing to be done about it but let them have their way!

Louise, I can see you so clearly in your garden, and 'Old Age' tapping you on your shoulder. And not a creak from the garden gate! I imagine your 'Old Age' to be kind and gentle and the tap being a touch of affection. Let Old Age know that I will be coming and that I look forward to meeting her. I am certain the three of us shall get along very well.

Don't imagine I'm a vacationer and must see the sights. I'm coming to be with you, Louise. This is why I am crossing a continent and an ocean – to meet my dear, beloved Louise. I adore the thought of spending quiet afternoons with you. To be in the same room with you! I want to laugh with you, to kiss your cheek, and feel your hand in mine.

I thought of a damselfly and saw you skimming the surface of sleep. And you wake to the scent of ocean in your hair! Louise, you take hold of my soul and fly it to heights I never before imagined. I'm often left lightheaded from some flights and am forced to settle myself with a cup of chamomile tea in my Sanctuary, where I let stillness bring my soul back to earth.

What a treasure you are to me. I believe you and I exist in a place together, in a country that has no borders, except perhaps for a sweet-scented lavender hedge - which has plenty of room to pass through, and after passing through, you smell like lavender for the rest of the entire day!

Before coming up to bed tonight, I wrapped myself in a quilt and took myself out to the porch swing. After a while I turned the lantern off and sat in the dark. And then I walked from the porch and looked up into the night sky. My breath escaped me before I could catch it, so stunned I was by the brilliance of so many stars – more than I have ever seen before. There was no moon, so the stars were holding court.

I thought of Emerson wanting to know the language of Nature. In that moment, I understood the language of Nature. I am certain of it.

The stars looked down at me and wondered what kind of light I was, and I whispered back, I am one of you. And then I heard myself softly rephrase my words – *'we' are one of you*, I said.

You and I, Louise, are now 'we.'

I take great comfort in knowing that you and I both look up at night and see the very same stars!

The stars . . .

Farm Cottage
York Lane, Bishop Burton
Yorkshire, England

Dear Cecily,

I am so sorry to have to tell you that our Louise has passed on. She had been ill for some time but never spoke of her illness, not even, I believe, to her flowers.

Louise left this world in the place she adored more than any other, her garden. I found her on the morning of the 9th of January, lying peacefully on the bench at the bottom of her garden, beneath the blooming winter jasmine.

Our doctor, a dear friend, believes she must have decided to sleep beneath the stars that night. I believe she decided it was time she joined the stars. That would be like her, having her mind made up and then doing something about it.

The garden was under a thin veil of frost. I believe, though, in a way that only Louise could have explained, that her flowers were with her in their fullness.

The entire village attended her funeral at All Saints Church. Shops were closed. All Saints is a 13th century church that sits on a mound overlooking our village pond. The sun, that often does not show itself in early January, struck out like ringing bells as the service began, illuminating the walls of stained glass windows, filling the church with brilliant colors.

I could not have been the only one who felt Louise had somehow arranged that for us; she was so thoughtful in that way. There is not a cottage garden in Bishop Burton that does not have some of Louise's flowers in it.

I will miss my dear friend, as you will, Cecily. But we must be brave. Louise would not accept anything less from us!

I am sending a letter to Mr. Burrows, informing him of Louise's passing. You, no doubt, will see him before my letter arrives and will tell him the sad news. I feel, though, a personal letter coming from me would be appreciated. He seems that sort, and Louise and I were never wrong about the matters of a person's inner workings.

Well, Louise was much better than I with regard to discernment. I tend to hold individuals up to a strict moral code, whereas Louise was not interested in such measurements. To my benefit.

Louise kept your letters in a cherished possession – a cigar box that once belonged to her father. I will send them on to you. I am sending also a box I found among her things. It has your name on it, and I am certain she meant for me to put it in the post.

I also found the enclosed letter addressed to you on her writing desk. I am so sorry, Cecily.

Yours Affectionately,
Helen

My Dearest Cecily,

Do you hear it? Listen – there it is again. It is the flowers in our garden. What do my flowers say, you asked me once? They go beyond saying. They go beyond language, for flowers speak the language of the soul, and for that there are no words.

You have heard their whispers before, perhaps when you were very young, when days drifted into one another like faint afternoon dreams. But you have not forgotten – you have only stopped remembering. For once you have heard flowers speak, you are changed. There is no going back. It is just the way. There is no explaining it.

The flowers show us what we are, Cecily. They mirror back to us our own true self. And what is this "true self" you might ask? Love. Love! We are a verb, Cecily! We are an occurrence in existence! Once we realize our true self; once we know what we really are, it is impossible to be afraid ever again.

Go to the thickets and the boggy meadows, wade through marshes, discover toadflax, St. John's wort, mullein, and poet's shooting star. Be relentless in your search. For what it is you desire seeks you with the same passion with which you seek it.

You have your garden now. Let it always be your sanctuary, for truly to kneel in the garden is kneeling before God. Let your garden give you strength and peace of mind so that like the tufted seed of the dandelion you may fly with the wind.

Oh, to see the world through the eyes of a wildflower! Can you imagine the view! The conversations!

It is late now and I am growing tired. There is a full moon tonight without a cloud in the sky, and I can hear my brook running down its stony path. It is not a very big brook, but it thinks it is, and I have never told it anything different.

This is not goodbye, it is only the passing of one season into the next, and all seasons are necessary for growth. We would not expect to find leaves on our ash trees in December or crocuses in August. No, all the seasons have their purpose, and all is as it should be.

Take care, My Dearest Flower. You have given me the best gift possible – my garden will not die with me but shall live on with you! And if we are both willing, we shall meet one sweet-scented summer afternoon in our immigrant garden.

Always Your Dearest,
Louise

April 1911

Cecily Barnes

Diary, April 3, 1911

My Dearest, Dearest Louise,

I have heard the voice of flowers! You must have known all along and did not tell me because you wanted it to be my own discovery – so that I would discern it for myself and hear with my own ears for the first time – my own voice!

It is late, and I am in the garden writing by candlelight beneath all the stars of Heaven. I see your light and know that we are not so far apart, you and I.

Here is how it happened, Louise. I was in the garden raking away mulched leaves. I got down on my knees to gently expose from the mulch an eager delphinium. It was then I sensed I was not alone. I smiled, for I often feel you here with me in the garden. But this was different, and I stood so that I might better see. It was then I saw my father.

He was standing outside my little garden gate. The gate was closed with his hand resting on it. We both stood our distance apart. My father had never shown any interest in my garden, and it struck me both odd and beautiful . . . his hand on the gate.

I saw him follow my gaze, and he quickly withdrew his hand and shoved it into his pants pocket. His sudden movement caused him to

145

lose balance, and he stepped backward onto a molehill. He looked down at his feet and shook the loose soil off.

"Molehill," he said, and cleared his throat. Then he said, "It will probably be bigger."

"What will be?" I asked.

"Your garden," he said, backing up again onto the molehill, not remembering. "I suppose some of the flowers, those tall ones, they might be bigger this year."

"The delphinium."

"Yes, those." The familiar silence between us grew, and finally he made a deliberate turn, rounded the molehill, and strode toward the house.

"I have papers to grade," he barked, and his anger stung my face.

The sun was sinking, and all the scattered clouds were turning crimson. All around was saturated in a golden hue. I knew it would not be long and the light would be gone. I heard the accumulated exhale from the gathering hours of the day, and I remembered what you said, Louise, about your father, that "It didn't matter what he would have said, it only matters that I didn't ask."

He was almost lost in the shadows of the house, when I called out to him. "Father, will you come into my garden? I want you to. I have wanted you to for such a long time."

He did not turn, nor did he move. I faced the

setting sun and the last burst of brilliance in the sky turning into night. I heard the creak of the gate. He didn't wipe the tears from his eyes. I ran to him, and he cradled me in his arms, his voice muffled against my hair, saying, "There, there. There, there."

I hardly slept that night, so full of new life I was. I was at my mother's grave as the sun rose, and I thought of what Quentin said about being out in a field as the sun rose and feeling you're the person to see it.

A rosy glow spilled across my mother's headstone, and I traced her name with my fingers. I spoke to her through tears (how is it, Louise, that tears are expressions of both sadness and joy?). I told her all about you and how you told me that I must first enter into conversation with myself before I could hear the voice of others.

In the beginning I thought your seeds were for my garden; now, I understand they are for my soul. Did my mother send you to me, Louise . . . did she?

I told my mother about Isabella Percy, and how my father was becoming quite fond of her, and that she was a much better cook than I, and I was certain that father would live longer because of it.

I told her that I was going away, that I had received a letter from Mrs. Curtis informing me that, in accordance with your will, your cottage and garden have been gifted to the Parish and is now "Mrs. Beauchamp's School of Flowers."

A Mrs. Hall Watt also informed me by letter that the school is looking for a teacher. You must have told her all about me, Louise. She seems to think I know everything that you do about flowers. She asked for a commitment of one year.

Louise, you can imagine my excitement – and then my absolute panic! I was reading the letter to Mrs. Percy when the realization struck me! My immigrant garden?! Who would water, who would weed, who would . . .

Mrs. Percy told me I went white as chalk before she could assure me that she and Annabel would consider it an honor to care for my flowers in my absence. I was exceedingly relieved!

You should have seen my father when I showed him the letter. You could have blown him over with a feather! Quentin is graduating from Agricultural School in the fall and will come and see me then.

I must finish packing! Father bought me a beautiful trunk, and it's already almost full . . . of books, Louise! The books you sent to me! Tomorrow I travel by train to Portland, Oregon, and from there, journey onward to the east coast where I board a steamer and set sail for your dear England.

Oh, Louise, by this month's end I shall be there! I will stand at your garden gate and announce my arrival! I'm certain the flowers will be expecting me. I will sit among your flowers and listen for your voice there. We shall bring our voices together, Louise, and wherever a flower blooms, there shall be a song!

Forever and Ever,
Your Dearest Flower,
Cecily

AFTERWORD

Caroline fell in love once again with this remarkable story, after twelve years away from life in Oakville and Bishop Burton in 1910. These worlds came alive for her, and she wrote to her heart's content.

Stephanie edited, encouraged, was daily amazed at Caroline's genius, and was overall very grateful to be midwife and handmaiden for the birth of this lovely book.

Caroline made Cecily's lists of "My Flowers and Herbs" and "Enemies of the Garden." She also drew Louise's garden layout and Cecily's map of the route the letters travel between Washington State and Yorkshire, England.

Caroline's wonderful husband, Dean, drew the flower sketches, the sow bug and beetle, and Quentin's sketch of Cecily's garden swing.

Grace Peirce and Great Life Books wove everything together into the book you hold in your hands.

Photo by Dean Wood

Caroline Wood was born in Yorkshire
England and immigrated to the United States with
her family in 1963 when she was ten years old.
After living in Southern California for ten years,
she moved to the Pacific Northwest. In this rural
environment, her love of books evolved into a
bookshop, and her interest in writing took root.
She has two grown children and lives with her
husband, Dean, in their cabin in the woods with
their two cats, two chickens, and their dog, Pippi.

The Immigrant Garden ~ Letters
Stage Adaptation

The two-act stage adaptation of *The Immigrant Garden ~ Letters* premiered June 2017 at the West End Studio Theatre in Portsmouth, New Hampshire, a production of Artists' Collaborative Theatre Of New England (ACT ONE), Stephanie Voss Nugent, Executive Director.

The production was directed by Ms. Nugent and starred Catherine Colby as Cecily Barnes, Carol Davenport as Louise Beauchamp, Alan Huiman as Mr. Burrows, and Tinka Darling as Helen Curtis.

Please visit www.immigrantgarden.com to request digital perusal scripts of the stage adaptation and to apply for performance licenses.

~ Other plays by Caroline Wood ~

Full-Length
Somewhere Between Here and Heaven
Is It Destiny or Just Me
Uncommon Wings
Sisters and Brothers, Husbands and Wives
The Boarding House

One Act (one hour)
The Orchard
Isadora's Favorite Nephew

Perusal scripts of Ms. Wood's others plays are also available at www.immigrantgarden.com.

To order copies of the Second Edition of
The Immigrant Garden ~ Letters,
please visit www.immigrantgarden.com.